SHOEBOX TO SILVER

by

Stephen D Smith

To
Sam

First Published in Great Britain in 1999 by
Neville-Douglas Publishing Ltd,
Clumber Lodge, Hemingfield Road,
Wombwell, Barnsley S73 OLY

Love + Blessings
Tisha xx

FOR REBECCA

PREFACE

This is a book of two interwoven parts. The first part is written as witnessed through the eyes of Trisha the child and the second as I saw it and see it now.

It tells of an ideal and the belief of a child who was tested to the limit as she progressed into womanhood and continues to be tested today as she searches for her destiny.

I was moved by her suffering and the trauma which extends from those dreadful days of existence in Hong Kong to her stoic endurance of successive tragedies when those who became close to her left this earth for another place, as though subject to some potent curse.

I do not begin to try to explain, justify or much less sanctify her beliefs as this is a task for another book at another time, but what I have tried to do is to chronicle what has actually happened to her in her short but remarkable life through the eyes of an initial sceptic. This is not a story which has as yet achieved the so-called 'happy ending' but it must certainly offer hope for just such a conclusion, as she strives to serve the spirit without fear or favour in the best way she can.

I have learned a great deal whilst I have been writing this book and I will always be grateful for that. I hope its pages offer something to those whose lives are unfulfilled or those who believe they have been singled out to suffer life's miseries in isolation without reason or explanation.

I am convinced that there is a reason for all things and a purpose for us all to serve, but there is much we can do to shape our own destiny as we all have free will and the right of choice.   The important thing is how we choose to use it.

Stephen D Smith

ACKNOWLEDGEMENTS

The Author wishes to acknowledge the following:

BBC Radio Sheffield; BBC Radio Derby; BBC Radio Leeds; The Ernest Booth Trio; James Brandon; Isobel Brookes; Tony Capstick; Robin Colvill; Neil and Maureen Crossland; Terry Dobson; Tom and Gill Furniss; Christopher Good; Gary Hartley; Haworth Graphics; John Holmes; Graham Jones; Jeffrey Jupe; Bobby Knutt; Rory Leo-Smith; Peter Levy; Matt Lindley of Optical Radio Ltd; Andrew Markwell; David Markwell; Jeni and Guy Morton; Neville-Douglas Publishing Ltd; Alan and Carolin Oliver; Len Pigott; Michael Smallwood; Ethel Smith; Jennifer M Smith; Rebecca Eve Smith; Stagewear Unlimited; Deborah Stone Photography; Max Tuoey; Charlie Williams; Trisha, Kelly and Lee.

Stephen D Smith 1999
A CIP record for this book is available
from the British Library

ISBN 1 901853 51 9 Paperback

SPIRITUALISM

The belief that the spirits of the dead can hold communication with the living or make their presence known to them in some other way esp. through a 'medium'; the system of doctrines or practices founded on this belief.

The Oxford Dictionary

FOREWORD

I dedicate this book to all humanity.

I sincerely hope this book has given a little more understanding to you all. No matter what your life journey, and what path of destiny we decide to take, with all the trials and tribulations along the way, we may succeed with love and understand, without malice and bitterness.

'Shoebox to Silver Shoes' was meant to be written and I wanted to open up all the corners of my heart with the truth for all to share, and to show that for all the pains and sorrows you can succeed and remain eternally close to the higher life – the universal love that is the very essence of our spirit.

Whatever damnation or pain enters your life it is imperative you conquer with love and acceptance, and try always to have compassion for your fellow man.

It was upsetting for me to reflect back upon my life, especially my so-called 'childhood'. But I now accept and understand I had to endure all these experiences for the moulding of the woman and the Medium I am today. You can't possibly comfort others if you haven't felt the heartache within yourself. This bonds the empathy between one soul and another.

I hope 'Shoebox to Silver Shoes' will bring the fulfilment and understanding to you all, and bring you serenity, solace and peace no matter what you endure.

Some secrets will have to remain close in my heart and die with me as they are too painful to re-awaken. However my dear friends, I wish you all peace and contentment and may blessings go with you on your life's journey.

I would particularly like to thank my friend Stephen Smith without whose efforts, hard work, understanding and kindness this book would not have been written.

May God bless you all always.

Trisha

IN THE BEGINNING

The knocking on the convent door could barely be heard; possibly it was the hesitance or even the reluctance of the visitor, but it was some time before a nun recognised the tap-tap-tapping on the huge oak door.

The sound of creaking drowned the final encounter between human form and wooden panels, but as the mighty prison-like door gathered the momentum to let the bright sunshine into the grey yard, the visitor had gone; all that was left to evidence the intrusion was a new shoe-box placed precariously on the third step from the pavement. But for a word scrawled untidily on the top and sides of the container in fierce red ink, the nun may not have noticed the mysterious object.

Quite what she thought when she read the word 'freak' emblazoned on the cover, or more importantly saw what was within, we will never know. Perhaps it is best that we do not.

THE CONVENT

The Mother Superior was a hard-faced unsympathetic woman, whose position and calling had steered a course into a frugal and uncompromising lifestyle, hidden by the skirts of duty.

Her piercing eyes stared down at the contents of the box and then at the lid bearing the offensive title. She shook her head in dismay, almost searching for inspiration.

The roof was leaking, dilapidated areas of the convent required replacement and then there was the visit from the Diocese who was represented by a clergyman and two clerks, checking to see that the convent was functioning properly. Her attempts to balance the books had taken the best part of the day left available after prayers, and the presence of a newly born baby, undersize and underweight, was an unwelcome distraction.

When the makeshift cover of rags was removed, the Mother Superior and her lieutenants gasped. Their reaction was not consistent, for amongst them were other members with softer features who had nothing but sympathy for the little object displayed so pitifully before them.

The child was white and pleasant of face, with a line of dark hair running along the spine from the neck to the small of the back. The eyes were bright and distinctive and flashed almost in curious recognition, but the body was covered in a fluid substance, most likely to be spittle. The most remarkable thing of all was the sex of the child. She was a Hermaphrodite, an unusual condition which took its name from Hermaphrodites in Greek mythology. He was the son of Hermes (Mercury) and Aphrodite (Venus) who, according to myth, grew together with the nymph Salmacis whilst bathing in her fountain and this combined male and female characters.

There was a vaginal area in perfect form, but above there were testicles and a malformation, which could have been mistaken for the base of a penis.

The Mother Superior called for a volunteer from one of the new novice nuns to see her, who would undertake the commission of becoming the mentor of the newly born foundling. Sister Marina knocked on the door and waited for permission to enter. Her breathing quickened a little in fearful anticipation as she stepped into the study following a single word of consent.

The Mother Superior's eyes fixed upon the young nun, who was standing in a shaft of light projected from a chink in the curtains which caught the mid-day sun as it invaded the sparse and rather austere study. The novitiate squinted as the light caught her full in the face, fearing to move until the Mother Superior beckoned her forward.

Sister Marina was a kindly woman with angelic features, of tender years having scarcely reached the age of twenty. She had a bright smile which indicated not only a servile acceptance of seniority, but a childlike and generous nature which inspired love. Her eyebrows indicated the colour of her hair, a rich mahogany. She wore a loose fitting habit which looked as though it had been made for someone else but it was pristine and clearly new. Her task was difficult, not just in bringing up the child, but in surreptitiously enforcing selective segregation from the other children in the convent. The child's long-term welfare would be considered later, but for the moment Sister Marina was charged with her immediate well-being. She set about this task thoughtfully and lovingly.

There was an affinity with the baby, for Marina too was an isolate and different from the other nuns. Hers was to be a life of confusion which was to end tragically, setting the scene for the next phase in the child's life.

Sister Marina's first reaction to the baby was one of relief mixed with a generous degree of sympathy, and the desire to give of herself. There can be no doubt that the child's mysterious arrival gave Sister Marina the opportunity to give and receive love on a personal but secretive basis, which would not normally have been possible in a regime such as existed in convent life.

Fate had brought them together, just as it was to prize them apart.

The child adopted the name of the kindly sister, and thereafter she too became known as Marina. The good Sister warmed to her task with a remarkable and motherly aptitude despite the circumstances in which they lived.

The convent consisted of a number of floors, but only the rooms at ground level were accessible to the children. The stairs to the upper floors were cordoned off by a small cord or rope whose sanction held would-be intruders at bay and retained an air of mystique about the rooms beyond.

The ground floor held most of the activity from the sound of the first bell which rang with annoying rapidity welcoming the morning and putting paid to deep slumber which had been achieved despite the attentions of old woollen blankets that reminded cold feet of the necessity to scratch.

The water in the pitcher, even at room temperature, held a chill and the children shuddered as droplets fell from reluctant faces into the bowls beneath.

Clothing took the form of black skirts and white blouses. There were three sets of clothing and shoes worn at appropriate intervals to allow for the weekly wash. The daily routine was greeted with the silent acceptance of children who were disciplined against being children.

Porridge welcomed the visitors to breakfast, but young Marina's was taken in the privacy of her own room, with fruit in plentiful supply, indicating how unpopular it was amongst the diners who took their meals downstairs.

Prayers were taken in the chapel, for what seemed an interminable period, before lessons of English, history and mathematics were taught on an individual basis in the children's own rooms. The younger children received elementary education, but there was a heavy emphasis upon religious studies for them all.

As the baby grew into childhood, she accepted and adapted to the prison-like surroundings, for she knew of nowhere else with which to form a comparison. There were eight children in all, but the segregation continued but for two hours play, which must have been perplexing for them all.

The relaxation period was enjoyed or endured amidst the high grey walls of the east wing, until the return to lessons and then prayers were taken before the evening meal, again alone in her room. The next day's events followed in seeming perpetuity.

The discipline was strictly enforced by certain of the nuns, without reluctance. Long sticks carried single small leather balls, which inflicted great pain when used as a wand-like weapon, to bring to order any disruption, no matter how mild. This unpopular therapy decreed that children would walk and not run through the cloisters, and noise would be kept to a minimum to avoid an even greater punishment.

Sunday meant that the children could dine together, albeit under watchful eyes, but this was the ultimate extent of the camaraderie. It was at one such gathering that Marina met Christine, a child of similar years who had an affiliation with head lice. She gave of her friendship and also the indigenous population of the unwelcome invaders of the head, but thereafter there was seclusion, again broken only by chance meetings in the courtyard.

Marina knew that Christine favoured her friendship by the squeezing of her hand during assembly and prayers, but this artificial society forbade a sufficiently long contact to develop any well-meaning relationship.

There were visits to the zoo and similar places of interest, but it was the people seen there who fascinated Marina most as it began to occur to her that there was much more outside those walls than she first thought.

At night, Marina would return to the confines of her room to welcome imaginary friends and giggle at make-believe events evoked by the spectre of loneliness, and then there was the morning and the visit of the ever-watchful Sister Marina.

Her kindness prompted her to give way to the playful child whom she secretly acknowledged entranced her with her youthful loyalty, but there was something else, something intangible, within the good sister's grasp but beyond that of her charge which led to the affinity. There were many conversations between the two in the privacy of the room as they sat on the bed holding each other's hands.

When Marina reached the age of seven she had begun to see with extra sight; to witness all manner of things which set her apart from the other children. Her expression of events and what she had heard, brought a firm rebuke from anyone other than Sister Marina, ultimately ensuring that the secret remain between them to avoid the necessity of a report to the Mother Superior. The latter would certainly have considered the girl to be a child of sin, spawned of the damned. But a reassuring smile and the description of being 'special' kept the secret between the two, until the child herself began to understand.

The two friends would often play together and part of their games were the sweets oft hidden under the third towel in the cupboard, and always the third one in sequence. This other secret was perhaps the confirmation of acceptance that she was indeed special, with a gift to see what others could not see, hear what others could not hear and witness events others would not witness, with only the softest rebuke from that smiling face of friendship. Theirs was a truly special relationship.

It must have been confusing for this child with no roots in the past, and not even a knowledge of her own name, to live in her secret world of visitors, from who knows where. They would appear at night when all was still and silent and tell her of wondrous things that her mind was not yet ready to understand.

When young Marina was seven years old the good Sister spoke to her and took her into her confidence. She had no choice, but secured a promise of secrecy which could not be broken by telling her that,

"It is our secret, but one day it will be for someone else to tell".

As each day passed, she became more aware of what she could see, and so it seemed did Sister Marina. But time had run its course and the Mother Superior made Sister Marina aware of some information which the latter felt she could not then relate to the child. She neither knew how to break the news nor how to come to terms with it herself. Then one morning at the tolling of the morning bell, Sister Marina did not arrive. The pattern had been broken and the child did not understand why.

Sister Anna, one of the older nuns, had no explanation as she prompted Marina to her breakfast. Her command was forceful through spiteful eyes, which squinted as she waited by the door. Her voice was hard and uncompromising, and her stare held the look of resentment.

For the whole of the day Marina searched and questioned until Sister Anna finally relented, more in exasperation than kindness. She explained that Sister Marina had left the convent, something which the child could not accept, for there had been no 'goodbyes', but the constant requests and questions caused Sister Anna to stop and look deeply into the child's eyes, and with a firm repose announce that Sister Marina was dead. For the first time during the exchanges about her friend, Marina was silent as she sat backwards onto the bed open-mouthed and desolate, which gave way to an unashamed outburst of grief. One can only speculate as to how this young mind suffered at the hands of such loss. She was inconsolable. She spent the majority of her time locked away in her room, refusing food and declining contact with any visitor who cared to call. Her only momento was the crucifix that Sister Marina wore above her habit which the child guarded jealously, so much so that it was to remain with her for the rest of her life. Those formative years sealed a special union so strong within her that she was driven to appeal to the spirit world in the hope that the good Sister might return to visit her.

Days passed, but the pain would not leave her. Her life had been limited in its exchange of love and affection, and such limitation made what she had that much more special and hence the greater the loss.

Her pleas for reassurance fell upon deaf ears and the following day inexplicably Sister Anna told her that her soul mate had hung herself by the neck until she was dead. From that moment Marina was entirely alone.

The days were long and the nights even longer whilst Marina waited for the return of the friendly Sister, but it was not to be. The monotony was broken by the visit of a man into this otherwise female preserve.

His appearance caused great consternation amongst the nuns and children; something was clearly afoot, but what?

Something told Marina that she herself was at the heart of events, and sure enough, just before luncheon Sister Anna appeared and directed the child towards the Mother Superior's office where she was told to wait until summoned.

As she was standing by the door, Marina could hear the muffled tone of voices, but the words were unrecognisable, until she heard her name mentioned. A chill ran down her spine as she placed her ear against the door. She strained to hear until the Mother Superior shouted the word 'Enter'. Marina caught her breath as she straightened her blouse before knocking and entering.

As she emerged into the sparsely furnished study, she felt the eyes of a new face fix firmly upon her. She focused on the Mother Superior, fearing a rebuke if she should look away, whilst desperately trying to view the stranger out of the corner of her eye. Her insignificance in this meeting was heartrending as the Mother Superior treated her dismissively and Marina was discussed like a common chattel.

She did not really understand what was being said, as her attention was fixed upon the visitor, and then the Mother Superior spoke to her. The only words she could associate with, informed her of her impending departure to live elsewhere. Her memory did not recall where, it would not have mattered anyway, it was of little consequence as the convent no longer held any affection in her.

It was then, that she was given the opportunity to see the man who by this time was standing by the Mother Superior's side. His large frame was illuminated by a table-lamp positioned in front of him, giving an eerie hue to his countenance. His form was frightening and threatening to this young child who had already lost the protection of the only friend she had. There were no skirts to hide behind. She was entirely alone to face the future.

He was tall and hard of face, with a number of deep heavy lines dominating his forehead which was softened by a substantial mass of bushy hair, but the thing she noticed most of all was a tattoo-like mark on his left hand. Marina had acquired remarkable powers of observation. Perhaps it was the incessant pressure to remain silent which prompted her to concentrate upon and develop this attribute, but her thoughts were disturbed by the man's voice which aimed itself at reassurance.   As he spoke, Marina studied his face and then his clothes, which were all of black apart from a full white collar, which confused Marina as to how it fastened.

Her recollection of his words was vague, but 'holiday' and 'new mummy and daddy' seemed like an inducement, and if they were, it worked, although Marina's experiences at the convent had removed any feelings of regret which she may otherwise have felt.

Sister Anna was recalled by Mother Superior and Marina was returned to her room.   The simple cupboard was emptied, and the contents placed in a small case, as Marina sat on the bed and waited. She was given a rosary, which Marina toyed with until Sister Anna collected her and led her outside. She allowed one backward glance at the simple apartment which had been her home for the full extent of her memory.   She thought she saw the face of Sister Marina, but unusually, it was not smiling. Little did the young Marina know the real truth behind her departure and the nightmare that was to become her fate.

Sister Anna closed the door, and turned and walked away as Marina's attention was drawn to the man, who beckoned her towards the door and into the empty courtyard.   It was then that Marina caught sight of her friend Christine hiding near one of the cloisters, and as Marina walked to the huge oak door, Christine raised her hand as if to say farewell. It was the last time that she would ever see her.

As the door closed behind her, Marina took a deep breath before walking to a waiting car. She was very much afraid. She had lived almost in captivity for the whole of her short life and she noticed the difference in the air which was unlike the musky smell of the convent. At times like this the most irrelevant details remain in the mind and in her case it was the convent steps which had worn away with years of use. Two leaves had blown against the step and in her disturbed mind she imagined they represented the relationship with Sister Marina, which comforted her until she turned to leave and a breath of wind blew them apart. Reluctantly she entered the car, but as it drove away she felt compelled to turn and give one last look at her only house of memories.

INTO HONG KONG

A ny journey to a child is a seemingly endless process, particularly when the destination is unknown, and so it was for Marina as she was sitting in the rear of the car with her humble belongings contained in a small imitation leather bag.

She sat nervously counting the rosary beads and found solace in The Lord's Prayer, as she looked expectantly out of the window, knowing only that she had embarked upon a long journey to a new home, and a family of her own.

Eventually the car reached a set of gates where all manner of vehicles had formed an orderly queue as they waited to move forward into a large car park. Marina strained to see beyond the vehicles, but her attention was seized rather abruptly by the sound of a low-flying aircraft, whose reverberations rapidly attained a disagreeable level. And then before the train of vehicles moved off, another plane, and then another, until the taxi moved forward with a jerk.

Once inside the car park the vehicle came to a halt at a further set of metal gates which opened and closed repeatedly when any intending traveller ventured near.

Her attention was drawn to hundreds of people, more than she had every seen before in one place, as they bustled to and fro, pre-occupied by thoughts of their own journeys and oblivious to the plight of this tragic child.

Eventually Marina's escort stopped at a counter, and her bag was taken from her by a kindly woman with bright red lips and unusually coloured hair which extended to a remarkable height from the top of her head to form something like a bird's nest. She smiled at Marina, who was staring at her in some wonder for she had not seen an airhostess before. Marina returned the smile that could not hide her confusion, but then the man strode off reminding his charge to follow hastily, as if they could be late. The man had spoken but a few words during the journey and even less in the big room, where they waited and waited and waited. It seemed an eternity.

The silence was broken by a peculiar-sounding echoing voice announcing an indiscernible message which mentioned the words 'Hong Kong'. It was then that the man stood and stretched before picking up his hat, and without a sound pointed to a further queue, this time at a smaller entrance with two similar looking ladies to the one she had seen before, taking tickets. All that Marina could think of was the earlier mention of a 'new family', and the fact that she had already missed two sets of prayers, and now she was to take the journey of a lifetime on an aeroplane, something she had only previously seen in books and in the sky.

The child was consumed with such curiosity, that she left a half-empty glass of lemonade at her table.

When the queuing process was complete two more ladies in similar dress welcomed the wide-eyed child into a smaller doorway situated at the end of a huge tunnel, which was large enough for people to walk along. Everyone was greeted with the same words and by the same smile, following which an apprehensive Marina was shown to her seat.

The long convoluted process ended with the ceremonial closing of the doors and then much later the sound of the powerful engines drowned out any thoughts as the plane taxied to the take-off point. The man had taken the seat nearest the porthole window, and as he peered out at the rapidly passing terrain, Marina noticed his hand and the tattoo-like mark she had witnessed before. There was a pause and then the plane rocketed forward, gaining great speed along the runway, until almost as if by magic, the huge machine left the ground and set off on its long journey to a strange sounding place by the name of Hong Kong.

Marina noted other 'outside' children on the plane who were sitting excitedly as fawning parents offered promises of delight in return for good behaviour. She too imagined she was embarking upon a holiday just like them, but there were no promises for her. During the many hours in flight she envisaged her destination as a fantasy-type place occupied by all sorts of kind and wonderful people who would laugh and play and not hit out with wand-like weapons when offended or annoyed. Sleep eluded her as hour after hour the monotonous sound of the engines droned on oppressively then night gave way to daylight, amidst a sea of pure white clouds which danced in the distance outside the small window.

At one point in time, Marina thought she had arrived in Heaven which she had always believed was some mystical place above the clouds somewhere in the sky. She remembered how Sister Marina had described the clouds as being made of cotton wool as they watched shapes emerge into fairy-like fantasy figures until one cloud seemed to transform into the image of an angel. But then a cultured voice announced that the plane would be landing in a matter of a few minutes, prompting the other passengers to make themselves ready. Her escort woke and looked around almost as if he had forgotten where he was as the stewardesses supplied everyone with sweets from a wicker basket.

Eventually it was their turn to leave, and so they ventured through a number of doors until they arrived at a reception area where, in the midst of a large number of people, appeared three in particular who were looking directly at her, as if in recognition. Marina felt the urge to grasp someone's hand, anyone's hand, but there was no one to whom she could turn in confidence except her reluctant escort who carried the curious tattoo almost like a warning, persuading her to suppress her natural instinct

The man recognised the waiting party and he strode towards them with Marina in close pursuit. Her heartbeat quickened in anticipation as she searched in vain to see those who had been described as her new mummy and daddy, but all she could see were the three peculiar-looking people standing before her.

She then began to realise that the majority of the people in this vast area all looked the same. They all had black straight hair, with discoloured faces and peculiar slanting eyes, which stared rudely at the young girl before them.

At the front there was a woman, small in stature, but huge of waist, with eyes which demanded the child's attention. Behind her were a man and a woman with similar faces. The man was older, thin, with discoloured teeth, which deflected attention from his eyes. He seemed to have more teeth than the average person, and certainly more than the quaint small woman by his side. She had a kind but troubled face, which smiled when her peculiar eyes caught Marina's. Their warmth made the child feel slightly more comfortable, but they spoke in a strange fashion with high-pitched voices, almost as if singing, but in a language unlike her own.

The trio turned and led the way out of the waiting area into the open air. It was difficult for Marina's young and naive eyes to take it all in. The sound of a thousand and one cycle bells, the hooting of car horns and high-pitched cries from a mass of similar looking people rushing to and fro, greeted her from every angle, whilst lights flashed on and off at regular intervals, proclaiming names that she could not recognise. Three odd-looking vehicles arrived without horses or engines, each guided by similarly dressed men wearing strange hats. Marina was guided into one of the contraptions, and with a tremendous effort the little man encased himself inside two large handles which lifted the passengers slightly backwards, before running off as if in a race, propelling them forward at a remarkable speed.

Marina's attention was drawn to a huge avenue of lights within which thousands of people could be seen sitting on the walkways and on chairs at tables left haphazardly at the entrances to a series of shops. Some were drinking, some eating and many with pipes and cigarettes peered out from long lines of smoke which drifted upwards without disturbance until passers-by wafted the smoke layers clear, only for the process to begin again.

The short journey took them to a place the like of which Marina had never seen before. The people who were eating and drinking out in the street made no attempt to move as the group disembarked from their vehicles and made their way to the building. They were shown to a table, and Marina was made to stand nearby at an entranceway to a larger room, from where she could hear strange music. She was drawn irresistibly towards the entranceway, peering backwards only to see if she was noticed. Her escorts were engrossed in conversation and were paying no attention to her, and so with each faltering step Marina walked further until she could see inside.

The room was filled with a peculiar sweet-smelling smoke which was emitted from a series of cigarettes and pipes which were being smoked by a number of glassy-eyed men. In the middle was a raised area around which people formed an audience converging onto the platformed area itself. The strange fragrance of the tobacco-like substance made her eyes water when it came into contact with her face. There was a continuous mumbling from the audience, which gently subsided into silence as two young people walked onto the platform. They were naked. The room was hushed in expectancy.

Then they lay together and moved in unison, in what appeared to Marina to be a most bizarre fashion. Shortly she felt her arm being taken and she was led back into a small room where she was made to stand whilst the woman inexplicably lifted her skirt and peered down at her underclothing. Marina was astonished at the differences between her and the young children, for this was her first experience of the naked form in anyone other than herself. The image of what had taken place remained in her mind.

The woman smiled and gave a reassuring nod and then Marina was escorted back to the table. She was hungry, and for the first time she made a request for food. The man placated her and said, "Soon," and with that they all left in a waiting car.

After a short journey they arrived at the gates of a large house with a winding drive; finally a meal of rice and other food which she did not recognise was provided and Marina ate voraciously, such was her hunger.

It was the first time she had eaten without prayers being said; something she had not realised until after the meal was finished. Her escort, the strange man, said that he had to leave but would return later. He was the only face she knew, albeit on a superficial level, and he was the only contact with her past.

The rooms in the house were pretty, with an abundance of gold and red, and most noticeable were a series of large vases, the like of which she had not seen before.

After the meal Marina was taken to an upstairs room which contained a bed, close to the floor. The lady who had greeted her at the airport appeared to be the owner of the house and she motioned with her hands to her face to simulate an indication of sleep but before she left she introduced herself in broken English as Ho So Ping.

As Marina undressed, her eyes gazed in turn at the walls of the pleasantly decorated room. Despite the newness of her surroundings and the sights she had seen, Marina was denied sleep in spite of increasing tiredness imposed by hours of travel and the confusions of a different culture and surroundings.

As the sun left the day the disciplines of the convent reminded her to observe the recounting of the Lords Prayer, which she repeated three times to make up for the omissions during the journey. It was a moving sight and a testament to the faith of a child.

A HOME AT LAST

The morning brought a refreshed bright-eyed Marina to the bedroom window and she rushed to open it to look out over a pleasant suburb with uniform houses surrounded by well-kept gardens stretching out into the distance. Although she did not know it at the time, the distance led to Kowloon.

She ate an unusual breakfast unlike the traditional bowl of porridge which she had been used to in the convent and then she was taken outside for a walk to the market place where she entered a world far removed from the elegance of the suburb where she was living.

The streets were full of lines of hawkers and vendors selling a remarkable variety of produce, unlike anything the child had seen before. Wide-eyed, the young Marina stared in disbelief at stalls with large green frogs in seemingly bottomless containers, and recoiled from live snakes waiting to be killed and skinned, but everywhere there was the smell of fish. Large cauldrons with their simmering contents steamed ever upwards on large makeshift stoves and everywhere the sound of chatter and ringing bicycle bells.

Decrepit apartment blocks of blistered paint and falling plaster overshadowed the streets, icons of a faded age, unlikely ever to return.

It was nevertheless an era of expanding economy, spawning demonstrations by young people carrying banners with pictures of Chinese political leaders, urged on by Red Guards who had infiltrated from the Chinese mainland. And then there were the saboteurs lurking in the shadows, ready to seize their opportunity by increasing the misery of innocents who were unfortunate enough to find themselves in their path.

Ho paused only to make purchases of odd-looking vegetables and considerable quantities of fish until they arrived at a delightful stall which was full of fine silks and clothes of all descriptions, managed by an eponymous street-trader with a curious but amusing name, something which Marina discerned from a heated conversation which she believed may have been about price.

Marina was curious as her attentions were taken elsewhere to a peculiar, completely bald man whose hands were enveloped around a lady's head in concentrated fashion. The lady was sitting in a kiosk doorway as the man carried out some odd sort of massage. Seeing the child's interest, Ho explained as best she could that the man was a prophet and could see into the future. When he had finished he caught sight of the entranced child and beckoned her forward to the empty chair. With Ho's consent Marina sat in the chair as the prophet proceeded to repeat what he had done to the lady. Marina felt excitement but didn't understand why. He spoke to Ho and pointed to Marina's eyes, but she could not understand what he was saying. Ho explained that the prophet had said that Marina had the gift of being a seer, a person who could see into the future. She used the word 'ghan' which was a reference to her eyes and whilst Marina did not understand at the time, the man predicted that she would have the ability to speak with the spirits. He smiled and nodded as Ho took Marina by the hand and walked further down the street to another stall where she had to use every ounce of self-discipline not to allow a smile to turn to laughter when Ho referred to the stallholder as 'Shui Pong'. The attempts at conversation produced some unusual words which were a cross between Chinese, English and complete rubbish, but Marina was learning quickly and was getting by with a mixture of memory and sign language which did not always fit the right place at the right time.

The stallholder held up a roll of silk in an exquisite red embroidered with gold figures resembling dragons. Marina studied its beauty whilst Pong measured lengths of the fabric against the side of the counter on the stall. Marina thought the acquisition was destined for a very fat person such was the quantity which Ho had acquired, but when they returned home Ho began to work, making beautiful dresses identical to the ones that she wore for special evenings. The dresses were tight, unlike the loose fitting garments worn in the convent, but she was enchanted by the colourful silks and unusual motifs which she had not seen before.

She disliked however, the Chinese custom of the binding of the leg which left her in discomfort. This process involved the wrapping of material tightly around the legs from ankle to knees to ensure that only small steps could be taken and thus 'enhance the eloquence of Chinese femininity when wearing the traditional costume'.

Ho's husband returned home carrying a huge briefcase which was so full of papers it was bulging at the sides. Ho stopped working for a moment and greeted him. She turned to Marina and spoke again, telling her that he was Mr Chan, her husband. He was a man in his early thirties but in his dark business suit looked considerably older. As he worked on industriously, Marina wandered to the back door where windows opened out onto a large garden, presenting an unusual feature for an island in which the population was soaring, and where the quest for land had placed a premium upon such properties. Compared to what she had been used to, her environment was idyllic, her new family kind, considerate and seemed to genuinely want her. For the first time in her short life Marina was secure, even if she did not fully understand the New World in which she found herself.

With each day she learned a little more and with it came an acceptability of her surroundings and a sense of achievement. After a brief settling-in period, a young man arrived who looked studious with thick glasses, jet-black hair and a tall willowy frame, which appeared to have outgrown its strength. His name was Lee Ling, and when he met Marina he smiled and patted her on the head affectionately. She liked him and his friendly smile, which seemed to take over the whole of his face. He liked her too and over the next months they became firm friends, forging an understanding which brought a great deal to both of them. Lee Ling could speak English fluently and he taught her Cantonese and Hap Ki Do, which aids relaxation, and despite the difficulties encountered in such an arduous task, Marina was an excellent pupil and she progressed into the language so well that she could converse like the locals. Ho So Ping added to her education with simple cooking tasks and sewing but Mr Chan was seen infrequently as the demands of his vocation kept him away from home for long periods and quite often Marina would not see him for days when his work demanded his attention. When he did arrive it was usually for dinner and thereafter he would disappear to his study with a large pile of documents which seemed to dominate his thoughts above all else, so that Marina was advised not to bother him lest he should change from the contemplative soul he appeared to be, to something else.

Marina's first birthday celebrated in Hong Kong was spent in what Marina referred to as 'the big house' and there was a party for some of the children of the locality. It was a lovely day, with a cloudless sky that greeted the excited child as she looked out of her bedroom window overlooking a well-tended garden which featured a bountiful explosion of colour just waiting to be picked and brought inside for all to enjoy again when the light faded. A warm breeze welcomed her as she skipped to the bottom of the garden where a makeshift table had been prepared with a series of glass containers which would later house a variety of drinks to be served at the party. No expense had been spared and Marina contemplated a series of lanterns hanging from the branches of flowering blossom trees, which dominated the boundaries of the garden's bamboo fences.

The clock struck twelve noon as the guests began to arrive, bringing with them gifts in brightly wrapped packages. It was a new experience for Marina for she had never before witnessed such generosity and kindness. The day ended with a noisy group of children who had lost their inhibitions pleading for just a little longer to play as a very young child vomited in the flowerbed after an excess of sweets and those marvellous things that look so nice and yet bring so much discomfort if abused.

When the last screaming child had gone, Ho So Ping called Marina into the house and the cleaning operation began. She was happy to oblige and saw it as a way of giving thanks.

Shortly after the debris of the party had been gathered in, Ho So Ping bade Marina retire to bed, but not before she hung up the new dress which she had worn so proudly that day. It held pride of place on the door of the wardrobe so that she could gaze upon it before slumber took her upon a dreamlike journey of remembrance of what had been her favourite day since her arrival in the strange new country.

The days which were to follow, formed an all too familiar but pleasing pattern and lulled her into a feeling of complete security as she lived out the time, blissfully unaware of what fate had in store just around the corner.

Within a matter of a few weeks Ho explained that Marina would have to go into hospital, as the time had arrived for her to have treatment to make her as other children. Her explanation was thoughtful and well meaning and Marina understood to an extent. Preparations were made at a special clinic and eventually the surgery was complete and Marina became as other girls.

THE DECLINE

Mr Chan was 34 years old but even to the inexperienced Marina he looked considerably older. Perhaps it was the work or its pressure and contingent stress which caused his illness, but whatever the reason it was more than a match for the unfortunate man whose torment caused him to leave this earth for a better place. Marina knew there was something wrong on the final day when he failed to set off for work with the ever-present briefcase, the immaculate suit and the shiny black shoes which gave way to sandals and short-sleeved shirts when the heat of the day became too much for him. Perhaps it was intuition, but Marina again encountered that feeling of foreboding which had haunted her in the convent and which disturbed her yet again.

Ho So Ping was distraught and there was little to console her. Her sister-in-law visited daily and appeared to take charge of the proceedings and what once seemed to be Ho So Ping's domain became her sister-in-law's and with it went Marina's security.

A few days later came the funeral. It was a strange ceremony, which resembled a celebration of sorts where guests wore white dresses and suits and there were flowers everywhere, tokens of faith and endeavour. A small capsule was prepared which held a small candle which flickered in the breeze before being placed in the river from where it made its way along the water's edge before drifting out into the estuary and to sea until it was out of sight.

The return home was conducted in complete silence and Marina was sent to her room from where she could hear the indiscernible muffled tones of voices. The morning brought silence as Ho So Ping went about her business with tired eyes, which bore all the hallmarks of sustained weeping. The ever-present sister-in-law watched intently as Marina helped with household tasks, fearing to betray even a token presence in case it would not be appreciated. She had learned in the convent how to be seen and not heard and it was an ability which was to serve her again.

Some weeks after Mr Chan's death the atmosphere in the house changed. Ho So Ping had taken to going out in the evenings, returning very late, usually in the company of men who would not return with her. The child was confused despite the reassurances of her mentor, but she had been used to conforming to a different regime with unpleasant sanctions, but at least with Ho So Ping she was given a measure of freedom which compensated for the inevitable periods of loneliness which haunted the household.

As the weeks passed Ho So Ping seemed to change from the pleasant thoughtful friend she was on Marina's arrival to someone else whose breath frequently smelled of alcohol and a sweet but smoky odour, similar to that she experienced on her first shopping trip in Hong Kong. The sister-in-law seemed to be always in attendance and at night there were unusual sounds unlike anything she had heard before, of men and women in some form of trauma or distress.

Meals were irregular and on occasions there were none at all, leaving Marina to fend for herself and once again the imaginary friends returned to speak with her just as they did in the convent. It was as if they did not wish her to be alone and in the absence of any other friendly face, she made them welcome.

Night after night Marina was sent to her room as Ho So Ping entertained her associates and each morning Marina woke and left to her own devices, she wandered around the house and garden. She had begun to notice that furniture had started to disappear and other important artefacts had left their possession never to be seen again. It was all too confusing, for the atmosphere in the house had changed from that which had previously existed. The lapses in concentration, the avoidance of basic housekeeping and the irregular hours all gave an indication of uncertainty and despite her youth,

Marina knew that there was change, and it wasn't for the better. One evening, Ho So Ping left early as usual but her face was full of concern. She looked into Marina's eyes with a knowing stare of reluctance and regret as an enforced smile gave away her thoughts. The following day a motor vehicle arrived and two burly men who disregarded the child as though she wasn't there loaded up the remaining furniture. She looked on powerless to intervene until all the contents of the house had gone. The clock struck twelve noon and almost as if by clockwork Marina walked into the kitchen to help prepare a meal. The room was bare and stark and the cupboards and drawers were empty.

When Ho So Ping returned she found Marina sitting on the floor gazing out into the garden. The beautiful flowering bush had lost its only flower. It was sitting precariously on the dashboard of the vehicle of the two burly men who had taken the contents of the house and Marina's flower as well. Ho So Ping looked to the floor, avoiding Marina's stare but they both knew that their time in the great house was short. At the end of the day Marina retired to bed or rather to the room where it once stood.

The following morning found her lying on the floor with Ho So Ping standing above her. With tears in her eyes she took hold of the child and squeezed her and avoided the questioning glances, which were entitled to be answered. Within the hour they set off and walked and walked. Once again there was no backward glance towards the lovely house which had been their home for so long. A feeling of déjà vu occupied Marina's thoughts until she arrived at Ho's sister's house.

The move to 'aunty's' took so little time it was hardly noticeable, but the salubrious surroundings of Mr Chan's home seemed a far cry from that in which Marina now found herself. Comparatively speaking, the house was smaller, without the welcome facility of a garden, and the furnishings were decidedly down-market in comparison.

Marina had lost the privacy of her own room and she subsequently shared with Ho So Ping. It was a small room sparsely furnished, giving the impression of being bigger than it really was. Interestingly it had a lock on the door, as did each of the other three bedrooms. The stairs led to a small hallway from which there were three downstairs rooms; one a kitchen, the other a dining area with the remainder, a sort of sitting room where Ho So Ping and her sister held their meetings and entertained a never-ending flow of guests, most of whom Marina noted were never to return.

The kitchen was much smaller than at the big house, but with the traditional cooker and stove and a large variety of pots, pans and different sized woks, all of which would have been the better for cleaning.

The dining room contained a table and eight chairs, only four of which matched. A window led to the street outside where the constant passing of travellers became more acceptable with the passage of time, until they were only to become conspicuous by their absence.

The sitting room contained an odd assortment of armchairs and a settee which had seen better days, with fringing which had become detached after years of wear and careless attention from Chinese feet. The walls were drab and badly in need of paint, with certain areas which would have welcomed some filler where cracks had been left to develop unhindered as they crept inevitably towards the ceiling.

There was one old painting, and a vase which was marked by a repair, running rather precariously from the rim to the base before branching off into a prominent pattern underneath.

The window was so placed that during the day it escaped the attentions of the sun, which kept down the temperature but increased the dowdiness attending the room's many faults. Marina always associated that room with the acrid smell of smoke and unwashed bodies which greeted her when she got up in the morning before a welcome surge of air met her as she stepped forward into the daylight.

The new lifestyle gave her more freedom, as Ho So Ping spent most evenings out until the early hours, which meant that she would stay in bed until after luncheon. In this precious, private time Marina took to walking, extending each week the distance she would travel, until she took to taking a small parcel of cooked rice and fruit for the journey. Her favourite port of call was the local church and the cemetery, where she found a sense of peace and the voices of the faceless ones who came to her. It could have been her imagination or perhaps wishful thinking for a friend or someone with whom she could share a confidence, but she seemed able to bring them to her in moments of contemplation.

One such friend had the peculiar name of Brave Owl and they had many conversations which always ended with an exchange of smiles and the comment, 'You are special'. He would also say that she would use his eyes to see and his ears to listen but she did not understand what he meant. She had lost contact with the children from the area of the big house and now she found herself very much alone, with even more reason to visit her friends whom others could not hear. The initial restraints imposed by Ho So Ping had gone, and whilst she felt some measure of disquiet, it was more than made up for by the gift of freedom. At first, her thoughts often returned to the convent and its strict regime, which made her shudder and possibly appeased the growing feeling of concern at Ho So Ping's obvious decline. Her sanctuary became her wanderings, and the ever-growing list of ethereal visitors who sought her company. All manner of strange callers came to her, some of whom spoke in whispers but made little sense, disappearing as quickly as they had come when their point had been made. Significantly they cast no shadows.

As the time passed, the voices became louder and the conversations longer, bringing with them an increasing understanding to this child with the ability to speak to those that others could not see.

Marina began to hate the evenings, with the constantly changing male visitors who brought with them strange mixtures for the pipes, and bottles of turbid liquid often left in half-empty glasses laid about the room for collection the following morning. Meals became more sporadic, with Marina becoming more and more responsible for herself. Ho So Ping's powers of attention had wavered and Marina found she was able to disappear for the whole day, providing she was in her room by early evening so as not to disturb the guests who claimed priority.

One night she woke with a start, and seeking a cup of water to quench a raging thirst, she wandered downstairs. She opened the door carefully and slowly, as if some premonition was warning her as to what lay beyond. She closed it quickly on seeing a fat, balding man seemingly wrestling with Ho So Ping and holding her down, and yet she was laughing out loud undeterred and oblivious to questioning glances from her ward. Marina returned to the seclusion of her room, but unable to find sleep a bright illuminated figure came to her as though through the very door itself which had remained firmly shut. The figure was nun-like and the resemblance to Sister Marina was remarkable. It was a dreamlike happening, far removed from anything that she had experienced before. She found sleep easily after this wonderful visitation, happy in the belief that Sister Marina was still with her.

Each morning, she would open up the house to disperse the pungent smell of smoke before she sought her escape to meet with her 'friends'.

One day upon her return she found the house empty of furniture but for one item just as it had been at the big house. Ho So Ping was sitting on the remaining chair with her head inclined at the floor in concentration. She paused before lifting her head on sensing Marina's presence and explained to her that they were moving again, but only temporarily until things improved. Quite how they could improve was anyone's guess. Aunt Heung had disappeared mysteriously, having 'gone away for a holiday', which Marina thought odd for there had been no family holiday since her arrival in Hong Kong.

A short rickshaw ride took Ho So Ping and Marina to the waterfront with their entire possessions gathered together in one large bag and then a boat trip to the harbour at Kowloon. They were met by an untidy man in a Chinese hat who was indistinguishable from all the others on the waterfront, except for a row of golden capped teeth which glinted in the sunlight as he smiled a twisted smile. He had a short conversation with Ho So Ping out of earshot but Marina realised that she had been mentioned because the man looked at her with a stare which made her feel uncomfortable. He was shaking his head and Ho So Ping was remonstrating with him. The conversation continued for some seconds until it appeared that Ho So Ping was tendering some sort of plea. The Chinese gentleman shook his head in what appeared to be a quiet and yet reluctant acceptance, and Ho So Ping bade the child forward with something of a smile, before leading her onto the waterfront.

The area was unlike anything she had seen before. She sensed scrutiny by a thousand eyes, which peered out almost accusingly as if they were watching intruders, and a feeling of foreboding came upon her causing her to shudder as she looked from side to side at the austere surroundings. There were people of all ages sitting, waiting and watching as they had done for as many years as they could remember. There was a row of corrugated one-storey buildings on an almost endless line stretching the whole length of the waterfront.

There were market traders of many callings selling their wares to all comers, predominately the waterfront people, but there was a certain distinction between this class of personage and that of the people at the big house and Marina was bright enough to realise that. They were simply not the same.

The so-called house was nothing more than a shanty-type shed situated half on land and half in the river, which part was supported by two wooden stilts. There was one room which contained a small area at the side for a toilet, in the form of a box of chemicals. This would subsequently find itself in the river and thence would flow to the sea. There was a bamboo roof, which was makeshift in design, but served the purpose for which it was intended. There being little rain during the year, it was adequate for satisfying its main function of keeping out the sun. When all was said and done, it was a simple shed.

The occupants of the waterfront dwellings were either at work or sitting outside their homes filleting fish or preparing vegetables for the market.

Doll makers and creators of all manner of nick-nacks were sitting cross-legged, working away at their chosen tasks. Meals were taken at the side of the street, with delicacies of duck feet and rice and soups of all manner of preparations, including birds' nest and sharks' fin. At night the occupants would sit in the street, talking over the events of the day whilst eating from chipped bowls a mixture of rice, vegetables and such fish which had been left after filleting, and everywhere, the smoke from a thousand pipes and cigarettes filled the night air with heady and sweet-smelling aromas. Some of the occupants would return from their day's labour in the factories and would simply sit in the river to cool tired and aching bodies. There were bars which sold alcohol and strange sorts of tobacco which had an intoxicating smell and then there were women dressed in tight-fitting, cheap clothes, with cheeks heavy with rouge, shouting at the male passers-by and giggling when their comments were returned. The constant sound of the sitar dominated the background with its pulsating music, adding a touch of mystique to an otherwise depressing arena.

Each night Ho So Ping would make herself ready with the same red tight fitting dress and an abundance of rouge which dominated her face, giving her a doll-like appearance. She would make her way the short distance along the waterfront to the local bar, where the Chinese gentleman possessed of what Marina had previously noted were 'golden teeth' would greet her. Marina would walk with her to the club and sit outside and play with one or two other children whose mothers were similarly disposed. The other women were of varying ages, from the very young of some fourteen years to Ho So Ping's age group, but none older.

The bar was dingy and contained a number of inferior plastic tables and chairs, patronised by a seedy group of Chinese men who mumbled seemingly incoherent requests from non-smiling faces to ladies who disappeared out of sight and then returned with trays of drinks and tobacco. The ladies were huddled around the bar, giggling and observing the men, until they were approached by the golden-toothed Chinese gentleman, and from there they would climb the even dingier stairs with whomsoever of the patrons chose to take them. It was too much for the young girl to understand, and when she enquired of Ho So Ping for an explanation, she was told that it was purely a game which adults played, but it provided money for Ho So Ping to buy their food and pay for their lodging. The innocence of youth forbade Marina to seek further explanation.

Initially she would sit outside by the entrance to the club, and together with her new-found friends would partake of bowls of rice and soft drinks sent out by Ho So Ping and the other mothers until, overcome by weariness, Ho So Ping would appear and they would wander the short distance back to their home.

On certain days of the week Marina was left to her own devices at home, to play in the street with the other children and then long after a preordained time had been fixed for bed, she would return to the water's edge, and using one of only two keys she would open the door and lie down on the steel bed until sleep found her, only to be disturbed by the return of Ho So Ping as dawn was breaking.

It was always hot and humid, and each morning Marina would bathe by the waterfront before dressing and eating a small breakfast of assorted food and fruit. Ho So Ping would be asleep in bed, leaving Marina to walk as the mood took her. She had taken to wandering out of the locality and one day on one of her walks she came across a graveyard similar to that which she had visited when she lived at the big house. It was more of a garden of remembrance, where the ashes of those departed had been deposited and marked with a small square stone slab bearing a name and the dates of their presence on this mortal coil. Marina was fascinated by this place, for it was calm and peaceful and allowed her to sit on one of the benches and contemplate. When she concentrated, the voices came to her and she would speak with them. Sometimes they would take the form of an apparition, which would have an aura of brightness around them, and sometimes it would simply be a voice, soft and contemplative.

She would stay for an hour or possibly two before setting off back to the shanty that she called home. On her return she would often see other children wearing distinctly coloured uniforms, resembling those worn at the convent. They were leaving large houses, which Marina concluded must have been schools. The inevitable eye contact brought confused looks from the other children who must have wondered why it was that this poorly clad child was wandering alone and not at school. For Marina's part, she cared little for what they may have thought, for she was the lucky one not having to attend herself as the experience of the convent had left an indelible mark upon her memory. The cruelty of children was never more apparent than when the schoolchildren had passed her by and they laughed haughtily making unpleasant references to her appearance as they made their way to waiting taxis.

But for the tutor, who had been employed at the big house and her limited time in the convent, Marina had no education. She had become a product of the waterfront where the people were so poor they were unable to meet the costs of schooling and inevitably children like her were left to gain their knowledge from experiences in the limited world in which they found themselves.

Marina had not realised that the area where she lived was in any way problematical and she took little notice of the dangers lurking in the shadows, although she followed Ho So Ping's advice to go straight home on the main path and not to venture down any of the darkened side streets as a matter of course.

On one eventful night she was making her way home alone when she heard the noise of men arguing from a side street. Curiosity got the better of her and she wandered in the direction of the sound to witness an incident that she would never forget.

Despite Ho's warnings, Marina found she was drawn irresistibly towards the scene of what looked to be three men fighting. As she drew closer she saw that two men were getting the better of the remaining one, who had exhausted himself by his efforts to break free of his assailants. One of the others produced a machete and to Marina's horror he lifted the menacing weapon and cursed, before bringing it down against the man's outstretched arm. The inevitable contact amputated the right hand and he screamed a piercing and violent scream of horror and agony as he curled himself up in a darkened corner between two buildings.

Marina was transfixed and unable to free her eyes from the sight of the bloodstained hand, which lay but a few yards from where she was standing. A desperate and tormented face removed golden rings from two of the fingers of the dismembered hand and then noticing her appearance, he fixed a fearsome gaze directly at her, turned on his heels and ran off into the darkness and the anonymity of the shadows.

The noise had attracted passers-by and their presence seemed to bring Marina to her senses. A woman screamed and then there was confusion. Marina used the opportunity to leave the scene and slip quietly away, whilst the gathering throng looked on at the unfortunate man who lay semi-conscious in a pool of blood. Marina did not speak of what she had seen that night, but the memory of the incident and those tormented eyes haunted her sleep for as long as she could remember.

HO'S FALL FROM GRACE

There were occasions when food was not readily available. It was a period which usually coincided with Ho So Ping's inability to work at the club. From time to time she would lie in bed for two days and sometimes longer, as if struck by some strange malady. One day Marina was walking in one of the nearby streets when overcome by hunger she came across a street café with tables which contained bowls of piping hot rice. The temptation proved too hard to resist and on the spur of the moment, an outstretched arm from a hungry child reached out and seized a bowl. Unfortunately for her, a fat and balding Chinese gentleman wearing a heavily food-stained apron shouted out loudly.

Marina recognised the words, "Stop thief" and seeing the advancing cook waving a steel meat cleaver above his head, she dropped her quarry and ran as fast as she could out of reach of the aggrieved cook, who flung the cleaver in the child's direction in the forlorn hope of hitting her. Fortunately his aim was poor and Marina escaped physical injury, but her first venture into theft dissuaded her from future folly as the sanction imposed on such transgressors was out of all proportion to the offence.

Quite what the effect of this undisciplined and unsavoury lifestyle had upon this impressionable child is anyone's guess, but the moulding of her character on the long journey into spiritualism had begun.

At night Marina lay alone on the cast-iron bed, which ironically resembled that in the convent although there was more freedom in this oriental prison. Occasionally her sleep was disturbed by Ho So Ping's return, usually in the company of a man, when Marina was banished to a temporary bed near the corner of the chemical toilet, where she lay after drawing the bedclothes over her head, only to be disturbed by the sound of the occasional visitation to the toilet by a guest whose inebriation had removed all semblance of dignity or decorum.

After straining to find sleep, Marina found difficulty in rising, only to find Ho sleeping on the iron bed, her hair flattened to her face with drying sweat whilst a tightly formed fist grasped a bundle of bank notes in small denominations, which she would conceal in a waterproof bag which was then submerged in the safest of hiding places in the bowl of the toilet. It was this compelling instinct for survival which decreed this strangest of behaviour leading to the search for another dollar and another meal.

The months passed and by the time Marina had achieved the age of nine she had become street-wise and completely integrated into the oriental way of life. She could outrun most of the children in the shanties, and fight most, up to and above her age in some cases. She was adept at hustling for a few dollars and became expert at playing the favourite Chinese gambling game of marjong.

Her elders would marvel at her cunning and skill, and from time to time she was allowed to play with the gamblers at the club if she had enough money to enter. At first she provided a great deal of amusement to the gamblers, who enjoyed seeing someone so young with such pretensions at playing a man's game, but when she started winning, their opinions changed.

After one major win the amusement turned to resentment and Marina was shown the door, leaving her to play the wretched game with children of her own age; unfortunately it soon lost its appeal.

Ho So Ping changed from the house-loving respectable, respectful and dutiful young wife to a sad caricature of her past. Her petite body had become bloated with drink and other noxious substances, her self-respect had gone and with it the will to place herself above the membership of the gutter. The quality of her guests had also fallen from the occasional soirée with businessmen to the irregular and steamy visits from sailors and market traders of the lower échelon. Hitherto Ho was Marina's protector, shielding her from the dubious excesses of man's inhumanity towards his fellow man, but as her decline continued she was less able to focus her mind upon her responsibility and with her self-respect went her duty to her adoptee.

By the time Marina had reached her tenth birthday she had begun to develop into womanhood and so she came to the attention of many of Ho's visitors and particularly the man with the golden teeth. Ho's resistance to argument had gone and her common-sense and morality had been replaced by a confused mind, befuddled by drink and drugs and then one night such resistance as was left was broken.

Two men came to the dwelling. Ho showed them in and brought them drinks. Marina was frightened by their demeanour and so she decided to go out, but as she moved as if to leave, one of them moved into the doorway and barred the way. One man occupied the bed with Ho who inexplicably looked away as the other man led Marina to a corner of the room. Riveted by fear, she followed him.

Marina looked towards Ho for reassurance, but she reluctantly turned away. The man sat down beside Marina and put his arm around her, his face close to hers. The pungent smell of second-hand beer and tobacco smoke forced her head away. At first she thought she would shout out, but the man was big, heavy and strong. It was difficult to know what was going through her mind at that time, but there must have been feelings of fear, disgust and above all, betrayal.

As the sun peered over the top of the harbour buildings Marina woke to the sound of a thousand bicycle bells. The men had gone and Ho was in a deep, alcohol and drug induced slumber. Marina went out to the river and waded into the water where she bathed herself repeatedly and then she dried and dressed herself and walked around the market place, which appeared different for the first time. The sidewalk cafés and other places of play held no fascination for her but then hunger drew her back to the shanty, and on her arrival she found Ho on her knees bending over the chemical toilet retching and vomiting. Marina noticed for the first time that Ho had become quite old. Her hair was greasy and had coagulated into a filthy mess. Marina was unable to assist her and felt guilty at the feeling of repugnance which she felt had been caused by Ho's fallen state. Ho realised that there was a presence in the room and she turned and caught sight of Marina. As she tried to stand she found herself falling back against the wall. Too ill or too tired to stand, she lay back and took a deep breath as her head fell to one side but her face could not hide the look of complete despair and resignation. Whatever bond existed between the two of them had been irreversibly damaged the night before, and all that Marina could feel for her Guardian was a mixture of anger and pity. She turned around and without saying a word she left the shanty and began to walk without a particular direction for she had nowhere to go. She walked for hours, ending up in one of the harbours where she sat by the water's edge and despondently looked out to sea.

Her attention was drawn to the sight of ships and boats of all shapes and sizes and it was hard for her to imagine that within only a few days or weeks those same ships would be in harbours scattered around the world, perhaps even England. For the first time Marina thought in depth about the convent. Perhaps it was not such a bad place after all and ironically, for the first time in over four years, she longed for home.

Her thoughts were disturbed by two sailors shouting from the stern of one of the large ships moored on the nearby waterfront who looked down at the waif and stray as she sat there all alone. She did not understand what they were saying and she didn't really care so she paid them no attention.

As nightfall came she moved, fearing the unwanted attentions of drunken sailors returning to their ships, and her wanderings took her past scores of street cafés and small kiosks preparing hot food.

She had not eaten all day, but the thought of food was the farthest thing from her mind. Eventually she returned to the shanty to find that Ho had left for the evening.

She awoke the next morning to find Ho returned but asleep. She had not chosen to castigate the child for the daylong absence and may not have even realised that she had been away, but sadly Marina no longer cared. It was the start of her complete independence and the end of her relationship with Ho.

One man visited more regularly than the rest. His name was Heung. He was a tall and thin Oriental man with a singularly evil look about him. He had a gold filling just off centre in the top row of his teeth, which were heavily marked with tobacco stains. On his visits he always carried a small package which he left on the kitchen table before leaving. When he had gone, Ho would take the package and conceal herself in the toilet area for hours before returning to the room, her face pale and drawn and beaded with sweat.

On one such visit Marina was outside in the street and her attention was drawn to an argument inside the shanty. She heard Ho shouting and then a torrent of bad language from them both. She heard a slap and all was silent. Heung appeared at the door in an agitated state, looked straight at Marina and rushed off with his handkerchief held to his cheek. Marina walked inside to find Ho sitting at the kitchen table attending to her nose with a piece of cloth as it bled slightly. Ho bade Marina to go outside, pushing some coins toward her so that she would leave to eat. Reluctantly Marina reached out to pick up the coins whilst staring Ho full in the face. Ho shouted at her, insisting that she leave, but her tone was more gentle and more conciliatory than before. Marina ran out and wandered down to one of the food kiosks near the water's edge.

The following week Ho had been pacing up and down the shanty, repeatedly expressing her disappointment and annoyance at Heung as she waited for him to deliver her weekly package. The anxiety that she expressed bewildered Marina, for she had not seen such a display of concern before. It was true that he had arrived well past the appointed hour, but she didn't see any other reason for her irreverent mumblings. When he did arrive Ho seized the package as though her very life depended upon it, and scurried off leaving Marina alone with him. Heung smiled as he moved towards her and placing his arm around her shoulder led her towards the bed. He overcame Marina's marked reluctance, but this time she was more spirited in her objection to his advances. Heung's attitude changed and his eyes narrowed even further as he gritted his teeth and with considerable force, he took Marina by the neck. She screamed but he placed his hand across her mouth and using his extra weight and strength, he forced her into submission and with it came the abuse.

After Heung had gone Marina sat by the front of the shanty waiting for Ho's return. She did not arrive until the sun had risen. Marina decided that she must expose Heung but the only person from whom she could seek solace was Ho. Marina hated him and she cringed at the very mention of his name, which made her determined to tell Ho of her plight.

As Ho walked into the confines of the small shanty, Marina could see that the front of the ubiquitous red dress was badly stained with a mixture of alcohol and vomit. Her right eye was swollen and reddened and there was a hint of a smear of blood from her nose, which had been wiped irreverently onto her cheek. She was mumbling incoherently and when Marina went to her, Ho pushed her away. It was as if she was in some form of daze with her speech making little or no sense. She seemed to believe that some secret invader, who had chosen to haunt her, occupied the room. She fell backwards onto the bed and within seconds she fell into a deep sleep and despite Marina's attempts to rouse her she lapsed into unconsciousness. Marina knew that it was pointless to try to converse with the stricken Ho. Marina had not eaten for two days, and although she had suffered such trauma, the hunger pangs had started and she was overcome by weakness.

She emptied Ho's purse of what few coins it contained and set off for one of the food kiosks. She ate ravenously from a bowl of rice and pieces of fish, spluttering and coughing in her attempts to clear a fishbone, which had lodged in her throat. The kiosk owner witnessed the scene and immediately pushed a piece of soft bread into her mouth and bade her swallow. It worked. It was the first kindness shown to her in a long time and she smiled sweetly and thanked her saviour who then gave her a glass of a sweet drink. She offered a coin in payment, but this was declined with an even wider smile, which moved her to tears. She had lived for so long in a heartless and uncaring environment that she had forgotten generosity and common courtesy.

The regularity of Heung's visits increased to twice each week, bringing with him the usual package which Ho either exchanged for money or her favours. During his stays at the house he would stare at Marina and smile the same twisted smile. At first he would be courteous and offer gifts of sweets and fruit, which were readily accepted. The child had not realised that the young man had a devious reason for trying to gain her confidence, and indeed to an extent he succeeded. At first Marina believed that his behaviour was just playful as he would pull her hair and nip her gently on the buttocks.

On one such occasion he arrived at the house reeking of stale alcohol. His eyes were glazed, he was unsteady on his feet and his attentions were more forceful and more personal than before, leaving Marina feeling intimidated. When his efforts were rebuffed, his attitude changed into overbearing unpleasantness. Marina confided in Ho, telling her of her concerns, but Ho assured her that Heung was simply trying to be friendly. She did not seem to want to understand.

Marina's eleventh birthday passed without incident, but there was no party like at the big house and she was devoid of presents. She lay awake in her bed and heard the pitter-patter of the rain on the makeshift roof as it leaked. Ho was asleep and oblivious to the annoying, repetitive sound of large droplets of water falling with remarkable precision onto the wooden floor. Marina placed pans in convenient places and listened as the water continued to collect as it squeezed itself through invisible holes in the roof before flooding into the receptacles which were dutifully lined up around the room. The rainfall increased and so did the contents of the containers, so much so that water spilled over the sides and onto the floor. Marina watched as first one and then another reached its maximum.

It was a birthday to forget and Marina had never been so miserable until her thoughts were disturbed by the sound of footsteps moving closer to the door. She shivered as the door opened. A large figure dominated the doorway, highlighted by the daylight from behind him in the street. He laughed as he entered. He was noisy and not in complete control of his senses and Marina recognised him. It was Heung and he was drunk.

He placed a package of white powdery substance on the table and turned and stared directly into the child's eyes before moving towards her, causing her to shy away. He laughed as he sat beside her. Heung reached out in her direction but Marina pushed his hands away, and then his attitude changed and the smile disappeared from his face as he gritted his teeth and mumbled incoherently. Marina got up in an attempt to run out, but he seized her and pulled her back down onto the bed and then the abuse began and she struggled violently, resisting as best she could, but then Heung, tiring of her fortitude, struck her a single blow with his fist to the side of her face.

The pain was intense and almost immediately Marina sensed that her nose had begun to bleed as spots of blood splashed upon her clothing prompting Heung to laugh. It seemed to spark further acts of violence and Heung continually slapped her about the face forcefully causing the blood to run into her eyes. She was powerless to resist and Heung seized his opportunity and performed unnatural acts with the forlorn and stricken child whose cries for mercy were regarded with amusement and contempt. All she could think of was to repeat the prayer she had been taught in the convent.

The pain was so intense that Marina believed that she would die. Her torment was so great that she almost gave up in despair. Quite what must have gone through her mind at that time is hard to imagine, but then she caught sight of a small box at the side of the bed which acted as a drawer. A small kitchen knife lay on the top of it, which Marina had used to prepare fruit for eating. Seizing it she attempted to ward him away from her. Heung reacted by taunting her and laughing, calling her offensive names and mocking her cheap clothing and her shanty home. He moved towards her his fists clenched and ready to continue his obscene brutality. With her vision blurred and confusion and panic reaching its height, she struck out with the knife. It struck Heung's body and he fell backwards onto the bed with his back to the wall. A patch of blood appeared on his trousers beneath his waist, which grew ever larger as a deeply shocked Heung looked desperately at her. As she wiped the blood from her face she began to see what was happening in front of her. She looked in terror as she saw the stricken Heung, his eyes closing as the loss of blood weakened him. He was transfixed as if time was standing still, with a look of shock and horror on his face, which would live with Marina for the rest of her life. It may only have been a moment but it seemed like an eternity as Marina looked on while Heung slid to one side holding his lower abdomen whilst blood oozed through his fingers and then, with a gasp he fell unconscious. It was at that moment that Marina came to her senses and seizing the opportunity she ran out of the house, taking the knife with her.

She ran to the local graveyard and sat by a grass bank, looking out over the stones of remembrance, hoping that her faceless friends might come to her and offer some solace. A man in an ill-fitting and torn uniform, who appeared to be some form of official of the cemetery, disturbed her. He spoke to her in a dialect which she could not fully understand. Fearing a rebuke and thinking the worst, she simply ran off. It is unlikely that he meant any harm, but Marina was finding it very difficult to cope. The voices became louder and louder and more confusing. Imaginary trumpets penetrated her awareness to merge with the voices of the street vendors and a thousand cyclists, all of which resounded in her head. She ran until she reached the edge of a small hill a thousand feet above the rocks below. As she looked down, the culmination of all the noise and trauma seemed to draw her to the edge. The rocks seemed to beckon to her, almost inviting her to jump, and then inexplicably just as everything reached a crescendo, it stopped. The knife slipped from her hand and crashed against the rocks below.

Marina caught her breath as she moved to the edge of the ledge. What followed was the most bizarre and extraordinary happening ever to take place in her life. It will be a never-ending debate as to whether it happened in reality or in the child's mind, but her sincere recollection was that faced with the enormity of what had happened, she decided that she could not go on. En route she had collected a begonia similar to that she had carried at Mr Chan's funeral where it had held special significance. She did not falter as she launched herself from the edge of the hill onto the rocks below, but fate had decreed further tests for this remarkable child as two ghost-like hands stretched out and caught her, placing her back on the top of the hill unharmed. A young boy who was wandering the area had witnessed the miracle, and Marina remembered looking into his face, whether for assistance or for inspiration she knows not, but he was frightened and turned on his heels and ran away.

OUT OF HONG KONG

Marina remained with her thoughts until dusk when she wandered back to the shanty. It was a fateful journey for on her return she found Ho sitting at the kitchen table with her head in her hands, accompanied by two policemen and a stern-faced, rather large policewoman with the look of an ageing headmistress about her. As the door opened the group were alerted as if being brought out of a trance.

Ho ran to the child but she was stopped by the large woman as the police beckoned her forward. She was taken by the arm and made to sit on a chair, and then came the questions. Marina did her best to relate the incident and as she did so she turned away from the sight of the bed and the bloodstained wall which was all that remained to evidence the horror of what had happened there. Within a short time Marina was taken outside to a waiting car which sped off to the local police station. She was taken inside and past the cell area where a number of fierce and suspicious faces looked on accusingly from behind a row of cells. It was dark and dingy, the pungent smell of urine invading every pocket of air.

Marina was taken to an office where she was made to stand before an old man with grey hair and a well-worn face, who was wearing a poorly tailored uniform which displayed perspiration stained areas under the armpits and around the collar. He questioned the girl about the incident as the policewoman looked on awaiting her turn to join in on the flurry of questions which had the child confused. Marina answered the questions dutifully, explaining as best she could just what she had endured over the months and years that the abuse had taken place.

The old man listened intently and at one point seemed almost sympathetic, before he shrugged his shoulders and then with a great deal of effort prized his huge body out of a chair too small for its purpose and left the room. The policewoman looked on impassively, without speaking. There was so much turmoil in the child's head that she could not think of anything to say.

After what seemed an eternity the old man returned shook his head and took the child away into an adjoining room.

There was no explanation, and with little or no formality he urged Marina to the door where she was taken to a second-rate cell in which a bowl of rice and assorted vegetables were waiting for her on the top of a small filing cabinet adapted for use as a table. She drank from a small glass of water, but before she could begin to eat she sat on the edge of the bed completely alone, and began to cry. A policeman passing by heard the noise from the room, stopped and listened for a moment before walking off to continue his business.

The following morning the policewoman opened the room door and looked inside. Marina was still sitting on the side of the bed, sleep having proved impossible. Her eyes were swollen with hours of crying and her mind was in total disarray. A sympathetic friend would have been the very least that they could have offered but this was denied to her. The policewoman snarled a command to collect her belongings, tapping her foot impatiently on the stone floor as she waited.

As Marina approached the door her arm was tightly seized, causing her to wince in pain. She was taken back the way she had come, past the cell area which attracted attention from the inmates, some of whom hurled abuse at the matronly figure as she marched her charge to the door.

Confused but compliant Marina got into the back of a waiting car. The driver smiled at the child but was admonished by her escort who waved him away as if he was of little worth. Shortly afterwards a young officer came out of the police station and bowed before handing over a large envelope which was snatched out of his grasp by the impatient policewoman, who then hit the driver on the shoulder and ordered him to drive off.

Marina had no idea what was to become of her and at that moment she yearned for a sympathetic ear. She would have been delighted even to see Ho, anyone with whom she could converse and seek answers to so many questions. What had happened to Heung? What was going to happen to her? Would she go back to the shanty or to prison?

She looked at the policewoman who was looking straight ahead impassively as the driver made his way past every conceivable encumbrance along the chosen route. Marina's heart skipped a beat as the car drove in familiar terrain near to the shanty which had been her home. She saw the food kiosks, which she had frequented so often, and recognised the street vendors with whom she had mixed and played marjong. And then in the distance the shanty came into view. It was sealed off by a plastic ribbon seemingly encasing the area immediately surrounding the building supported by poles held in place by moulded bases. As the taxi passed by she turned to see if she could see Ho which earned a stern rebuke from her would-be gaoler.

Within minutes the car was speeding past the cemetery which had been Marina's haven in her moments of solitude, but she did not look back for fear of a further reprimand. Eventually the car arrived at the gates to the airport which sent the child's mind racing.

The car stopped abruptly at the large doors marked 'Departures' and the driver hurried to open the policewoman's door. He then ran round to the other side of the vehicle with a view to letting Marina out but at first she did not move, until on a word of command from the ogre she was prompted to leave, now more confused than ever. Why was she being brought to the airport? Her curiosity and concern got the better of her and she blurted out her question to the formidable but otherwise silent companion who stopped in her tracks. For the first time she looked at Marina and stared into her eyes, and with a sarcastic smile she told her she was going home to England. Marina was speechless. She was grabbed by the arm and pulled along like an awkward child who had tried her parents' patience too far.

Perhaps this was the punishment for the awful incident with Heung, or so Marina thought, but then what of Ho? Although the relationship had soured by reason of the woman's conduct there was a depth of feeling for she was the only 'parent' Marina had known since Mr Chan's death. It was the final insult not to be there to see her go.

As they reached the passport control the policewoman handed over a set of papers which a sombre-looking official scrutinised most carefully. He looked at Marina and then back at the papers and then at her escort, who mumbled under her breath clearly annoyed at yet another delay. The man then used his telephone and spoke in an unusual dialect which Marina could not follow, and after a short discussion he replaced the handset and nodded at the policewoman, stamping the papers with an object from his drawer. He handed the documents to Marina and indicated contemporaneously that she should place them inside the small bag which she was carrying. A moment later a pleasant well-groomed European lady in bright red uniform came through the departure lounge doors and beckoned to her. Marina turned and looked at the policewoman who ushered her forward with complete disdain, then promptly turned and walked away without so much as a word or a backward glance.

Marina walked slowly towards the attractive lady, resplendent with long blonde hair and engaging smile to be rewarded by a friendly arm placed on her shoulder and the welcoming words of an English greeting. Marina responded, although she found it difficult to remember her English for she had not used the language since her days with the tutor at the big house.

It was true she was going to England, but where would she live? She wondered whether she was going to prison but then her thoughts went back to Ho. How could she leave her without saying goodbye?

As she walked into the lounge she was asked to sit at a table and the smiling escort handed her a doll with a Chinese face to play with, but Marina was becoming distraught. The kindness which was being shown to her, prompted her to query her fate. The lady looked at her and smiled and told her that she was going home and that everything would turn out for the best. A new home would be waiting with new friends and above all, a happy life. For all that Marina was young she had grown streetwise and knew that a smile could often conceal deceit. Marina was unable to believe her.

A distorted voice announced the departure of a flight to London and the young lady reappeared and took her gently by the hand. They walked to the main doors where an airport bus began the short journey to the plane. All that remained of Marina's life in Hong Kong, apart from her bag containing a few clothes, was a small Chinese doll which remained on the chair in the airport lounge where she had left it.

Just as she was climbing the stairs onto the plane a familiar face appeared at the observers window in the public visitors lounge, frantically beating on the window with her hands. It was Ho. Somehow she knew what was happening. She was intent upon getting through to Marina but her cries were drowned by the sound of the aeroplane engines, which roared in salute to the waiting passengers below.

Marina watched helplessly as she saw the policewoman approach Ho from behind and take her by the arms in an attempt to pull her away from the window but Ho was not to be denied and she fought furiously only to be restrained by two policemen who came to assist.

Marina was beckoned onto the top of the stairs and into the plane, but not before she was able to turn and catch one last glimpse of Ho's distraught face and then in an instant she was gone. The tearful Marina was taken to a seat at the rear of the plane near to where the airhostess was to sit for take-off. Within a matter of only a few minutes the plane taxied to the runway and set off past the observation tower and into the sky. Marina was never to see Ho again.

BACK TO ENGLAND

It was a long flight lasting approximately fourteen hours during which time the blonde-haired hostess spent as much time as she could with her charge. At one point there was severe turbulence causing all the aircrew to be confined to their seats and during that time they had a long conversation. Marina was told that owing to her circumstances in Hong Kong and the fact that it was thought that Ho could no longer look after her properly, the authorities took the view that it would be better if she were to return home. She was told that someone would be waiting for her in England and would take her to a new home. Although the child did not fully appreciate it, it was a heartless act to leave her with such uncertainty.

When the plane arrived in England Marina was tired and hungry. She had been unable to eat the meals provided on the plane because she had been used to simple Chinese food and the taste of European dishes had long since left her memory.

As she left the plane the hostess hugged her and assured her that she would be well looked after. At the entrance to the airport doors she turned and waved to her new found friend, and thought she saw a hint of a tear in her eyes. Clutching the papers which the policewoman had given to her, she entered passport control and on her arrival the man at the counter picked up his telephone, just as his Chinese counterpart had, and appeared to be speaking about her. Shortly afterwards she was taken by a member of staff through the reception doors and into a large sitting area where she was greeted by the sight of a huge number of people carrying boards upon which names were inscribed to assist contact with travellers entering the foyer.

Marina saw two ladies who appeared to be looking at her before they moved towards her and asked her name. One of the women spoke in Chinese and Marina was able to converse with her. They both smiled and she was reassured. They told her that they had come to take her to what they described as home. She was taken outside to a taxi and then to a railway station where she was given chocolate bars to eat. The train journey lasted for approximately three hours after which she was taken by yet another taxi to a very large house similar in form to the convent. There was a large sign at the front gate which she was able to read and which said 'Doctor Barnardo's.

It was a large building resembling a country house, but in many ways it also resembled the convent. The courtyard was empty, but as the taxi pulled up outside the large oak doors leading to the main hall, Marina could hear the sound of children singing. As the taxi pulled away Marina was left alone with her small bag clutched to her waist and the music proved a moving greeting for this child of the Kowloon streets. As she listened standing before the great oak doors, her mind wandered back to the shanty and thoughts of Ho. But suddenly the doors creaked as they opened just as the song reached a crescendo. A smiling face beckoned to her and slowly Marina mounted the stone steps. She did not falter, nor did she look backwards. A new chapter was to begin and another stage in Marina's development greeted her with open arms.

AT DR BARNADO'S

The Principal was a kindly man of high ideals and a sense of morals. He was in charge of a staff of twenty. He was popular with pupils and staff alike and had dedicated a career to the Dr Barnado's Organisation which in turn had given him a measure of security and a great deal of satisfaction. The Home looked after eighty to ninety children ranging in age from two to sixteen years. Marina fitted in well but she felt the discipline difficult to contend with, particularly when she had been so used to the regular escape to her haven of seclusion.

At first she found it difficult to digest the heavy meals of meat, potatoes and boiled vegetables, but Marina was chameleon-like, having learned the art so well whilst in Hong Kong. After what she had seen and had been through, the Home did not present a problem to her. She got on well with the other children having established something of a reputation of being able to look after herself.

Unfortunately she was behind with her education and the art of reading and writing had almost disappeared from her curriculum vitae. She worried about classes because of the difficulties she experienced in catching up, but her remarkable memory eased the way through, avoiding embarrassment and the displeasure of her teachers.

The regime was easier than at the convent and the ubiquitous iron bed seemed to have been built especially for her, but she had her own room and for the first time in years, a measure of privacy. The settling-in period was difficult but was mitigated by her new-found ability to attract the other children to her cause.

One such child was called Trudy and she was Marina's favourite. She was six years old and a pretty child despite the loss of most of her front teeth and each morning she would greet Marina with the same toothless grin. She was followed everywhere from first thing in the morning to last thing at night with her only respite being lessons and sleep.

Trudy had suffered a great deal prior to coming to the Home because her parents and her eldest sister were killed in a road traffic accident and she was left traumatised. There were no other immediate family members who could look after her and so consequently she was taken to Dr Barnado's. She had lost the ability of speech since the accident, but for the first time she had found someone in the Home to whom she could relate, but no matter how hard the staff at the Home tried, they could not persuade her to speak, although she was bright and able to deal competently with lessons unless a voice was required in which case she would simply turn away.

The age difference and the absence of close family made Marina into a mother figure and slowly but surely the relationship with Trudy provided a necessary therapy, for them both.

Marina developed a Hamelinesque-type character and found favour with story telling. She was the champion of the underdog and the scourge of bullies. The younger children seemed to hide behind her skirt-tails and for once she was revered and wanted, but inevitably there were those who were jealous. Then as now, there were enemies born out of resentment.

One girl in particular was older and bigger and the only way she could stamp her authority and personality on others was to demand it with intimidation and violence. For a time Marina steered clear of her avoiding a confrontation, until one day, inevitably, there was a clash of wills. Tired of taking second place Cora decided that enough was enough and the constant chanting of Marina's name and the ever-present laughter from her entourage grated upon her so much that she decided to teach her a lesson.

Cora knew of the relationship between Marina and Trudy and so she deliberately and spitefully began to pick on Trudy with the sole intention of causing trouble. She would pull her hair, nip the back of her arms or trip her up and when exasperation set in she would slap her face as hard as she could. One day, Cora was seen to bully the child and Marina was told about it.

Cora was an unhappy child. She was illegitimate and her mother had taken to drink with the result that she was unable to care for her. She hated the Home and resented having been cast aside by circumstances, which led to her seeking solace in bullying.

One day Trudy was walking along the corridor near the main hall when she came face to face with Cora. A slap to the back of the head caused Trudy to spin around and face her attacker, which prompted a further slap from the embittered aggressor. Trudy ran off into the toilets and locked herself into a cubicle and it was some minutes before she had gathered herself so as to go back into the schoolroom. It was obvious to the teacher that something had happened, for she had detected something about her manner which had caused some concern, but Trudy was not given to crying and of course her refusal to speak hid her real feelings.

Two days later she was walking to the dormitories when an outstretched foot tripped her on the landing. As she got up she noticed the sneering

Cora enjoying macabre amusement on sight of a slight cut to Trudy's head.

The following morning the House Mother, seeing a blood-stained pillow, referred the matter to Trudy's form teacher. The consensus of opinion was that the child had suffered a fall although Marina took an entirely different view and for reasons which she could not understand something or someone warned her of Trudy's plight. At first she thought it was her imagination, but a further warning made her realise that it was a voice similar to the one who had visited her in Hong Kong.

Only a matter of a few days later Trudy was sitting alone on a bench in the garden of the house looking at a picture book which had been the subject of one of the lessons. She was holding a teddy bear, which had been with her at the time of the car crash, as she had taken to carrying it during the day. The school made an allowance and allowed her to keep it with her during school hours as it seemed to make her happy, but then as if from nowhere Cora arrived and seized the teddy bear, pulling off one of it's arms. Trudy tried to grasp the damaged toy only to be forcibly restrained with stronger arms when two direct blows to her face caused her nose to bleed. Marina was nearby and she had realised that something was wrong as a voice guided her to the garden and when she arrived her little friend ran into her arms, Marina rebuked Cora for what she had done only to be met with a tirade of abuse.

Just before breakfast the next morning, Cora waited at the end of the corridor leading to the dormitories. Marina was last to leave having ensured that one of the younger ones had got up on time and as she walked down the corridor Cora stepped out in front of her and hurled abuse including the suggestion that her mother was a 'slant-eyed chink'. Cora was three stones heavier and at least six inches taller with wrists as thick as any young man but as Cora moved towards her, Marina clenched her fists.

Five minutes later Marina walked into assembly sporting the beginnings of a black eye. The children looked on as they sang the morning hymn only to break out into smiles of admiration when Cora arrived displaying two black eyes and a swollen and bloodied nose. Marina winked at her group of supporters and joined in the hymn singing as she moved next to Trudy and squeezed her hand.

From time to time perspective adopters arrived at the Home and their visits caused much interest amongst the children. One such couple were a doctor and his wife who had been married for some time but had no children of their own. On their initial visit they had heard something of

Trudy's plight and were keen to try to help and eventually they were introduced to her.

They were a kind couple and despite Trudy's wariness there seemed to be some measure of empathy between them. Their meetings continued and the doctor seemed to gain the child's confidence so much so that they were getting on well. Trudy would often be seen to smile although the ability to speak continued to be denied her.

ADOPTION

The doctor and his wife were very kind people and it was obvious to all the staff at the Home that they would probably be best placed to look after Trudy particularly as the doctor's qualification in psychiatry would also help to try to unravel the complexities of the trauma-induced psychological problems which caused her silence.

One afternoon the Principal called the child to his office and told her that the good doctor and his wife were anxious to have a child of their own and she had been the one who had been chosen to go to live with them but he was anxious to know how she felt about the proposition before a decision was made. She felt a mixture of emotions, on the one hand there was a promise of security and a home with two very caring people whom she liked and felt safe with, but on the other there was her friendship with Marina.

The doctor lived a few miles away but had been promoted into a senior position in London, which meant the other side of the world so far as the child was concerned. The Principal explained that it was a wonderful opportunity and the doctor would try to help to make her well again. Trudy sat at the end of the chair clutching her teddy bear and it was apparent that she wished to speak, to say something, anything, but try as she might the words would simply not come out.

Sensing the difficulty the Principal posed the question in simple form, requiring an answer of either yes or no.   Trudy simply nodded but there was a reluctance about her which he could not understand.   He explained that there were formalities to complete and it would be some time before she would be able to leave, but he would speak to her again when the time came near.

She returned to the playground and sought out Marina and when she drew close she seized her hand and squeezed it tightly.   Intuitively Marina realised that something had happened in the Principal's office and once again Trudy tried to speak.   Marina took her on one side and realising the effort that her friend was making she tried to encourage her by asking what had happened.   Just then another couple of prospective foster-parents walked past towards the car park with one of the children.   The child was walking between the adults holding their hands and they were all laughing as though something had amused them.   Trudy looked at the trio and then back at Marina and almost by telepathy she knew what had happened.   Marina gave a reassuring smile and asked if the doctor and his wife had come to adopt her.   She nodded, but sensing her reluctance,

Marina reassured her with a hug and for the rest of that day she never left Marina's side.

Some weeks later the Principal sent for Trudy again and called upon Marina to find her. Marina realised why. The proposed adoption was such a wonderful opportunity and she knew that much could be done to help Trudy with her speech problems. Later that day Marina asked one of the teachers what was to happen and she was told that the adoption would be complete just before Christmas.

When that fateful day came the children were helping to put the finishing touches to the Christmas trimmings in the main hall. It should have been a happy time but Marina knew that this was to be Trudy's last day at the Home.

She went to her room and collected her belongings which fitted conveniently into a small leather suitcase which had seen much better days and when she reached the bottom of the stairs she was greeted by her form teacher who reassured her as they walked to the large doors leading to the front of the house. Marina was waiting for her and the two children greeted each other with a hug. Marina's feelings were a mixture of happiness and regret as she had formed a considerable attachment to her young friend but the prospect of seeing her with a caring family to look after her outweighed any feeling of loss at seeing her leave.

The doctor and his wife were standing in the doorway and they called Marina over to speak with her.   The doctor told her that he had been made aware of their friendship and of how Marina had protected Trudy from the bully.   He had a wide, broad and endearing smile and a kind face with sparking blue eyes, which seemed to shine all the more when he smiled.   Marina realised that he was a caring man and a friendly voice whispered to her that Trudy was to be safe and happy, but when she turned to see who had spoken, there was no one there.

The doctor told Marina that his friends in the profession were going to help Trudy to speak again, but somehow she knew that they would and she told the doctor so.   He smiled at her confidence, it wasn't just an earnest wish she actually knew it would happen.

When Trudy saw Marina she ran to her and grasped her as tightly as she could before turning to take the outstretched hand of the kindly doctor.   Just before they set off to leave she turned, ran back and hugged Marina once again and at that moment tears welled-up in Trudy's eyes as she began to cry. Marina held her tightly and whispered to her that she would soon be well again and would have a very happy life.   Then, with their cheeks touching in an embrace, Trudy whispered "Thank you, Marina." It was a miraculously precious moment from which Trudy's rehabilitation began. Pushing a small untidily-wrapped parcel into Marina's hand, she turned and walked away and a second later she was sitting in the back of the car looking out of the window and waving, with tears streaming down her cheeks.

The parcel contained a simple gift of an old teddy bear with a recent repair where the arm had been pulled off. Marina looked up and waved until the car finally moved out of sight.

Another vehicle arrived just as Marina was going back into the Home and two of the teachers got out accompanying a young child who was new to the Home. One of the teachers introduced her and asked Marina if she would look after her as she was very shy and nervous. Marina smiled. The child introduced herself with a dreadful stutter such was the difficulty she had giving her name. Marina looked to the heavens as if for inspiration before taking her hand and walking her into the main hall towards the twelve feet tall Christmas tree which had pride of place in the corner. It was beautifully decorated with bright lights which flickered on and off in sequence and at the top there was a golden angel perched majestically on the very last branch. The child gazed in wonder at the spectacle before her and then her attention was focused upon a box of presents set out neatly beneath the tree. She then looked at her new friend and her eyes sparkled as she caught sight of the small teddy bear which Marina was carrying.

That night the new child found no difficulty in sleeping. She had a new-found friend, and to her at least, a new but slightly damaged teddy bear for company.

Trisha pictured on the right.

Edna Smith pictured on the left.

Kelly and Lee, Trisha's children.

Jane pictured on the right.

Bobby Knutt, Lee, Trisha and Robin Grumbleweed hiding behind a pole!

Kelly and Trisha — The Palace Theatre, Mansfield 1998.

The author, Stephen D. Smith.

Charlie Williams, the Author and Trisha.

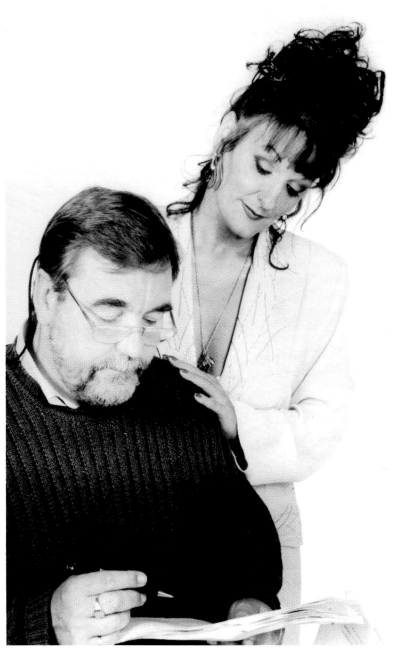

Stephen D. Smith and Trisha — photocall September 1999.

Trisha, September 1999, on the eve of the publication of 'Shoebox to Silver Shoes.'

A HOME OF HER OWN

The Staff at Dr Barnardo's were very caring and hardworking and they did their very best to encourage a homely atmosphere but it was impossible to create an exact replica of family life because the special bonding of parent and child was missing. In comparison with her life at the convent or in Hong Kong, and in spite of the constantly changing complement of children resident there, Marina found security and a measure of happiness within the confines of the Home. The younger children came and went as the influx of foster and adoptive parents increased, and it was always the younger ones who were catered for more easily.

Marina had lived in the Home for approximately ten months when a man called Walter Smith came to visit.

Walter Smith was reasonably well off. He was serving in the Royal Air Force and in addition he owned a fish and chip shop but his private time was well spent working tirelessly as a charity worker. He was a very kind and spiritual man with a handsome countenance and a generous nature. He had discussed adoption with the Board of the Home and had been passed as a suitable candidate but the difficult part was in selecting a child. There can be no doubt that whoever he selected would be most fortunate because his kindness knew no bounds and he was the personification of fairness and hope.

Edna was his wife and they had a daughter Shirley and all three were happy and content save for their desire to extend their family. The couple were anxious for a boy to complete the family unit and their regular visits to the Home were geared towards this purpose.

It was on one such visit that Mr Smith first met Marina. It was a chance meeting, or rather that is what he thought, but spiritualists believe that much of our lives are pre-ordained and so this meeting was destined to happen.

Marina smiled at him in passing, a compliment which Walter returned, and being quite taken with this mysterious child with the attractive face, he asked one of the teachers who she was. Her story appealed to his compassionate nature and on a subsequent visit he decided to make further enquiries. He was much moved by the plight and former suffering of Marina with the result that he asked if he could meet her. As he walked in their midst the children realised somehow, perhaps by experience, that he was a potential adopter, and this gave rise to a considerable excitement around the playground. Many of the children tried feverishly to gain pole position in a make-shift queue which had started to form around the visitors as they walked around the gardens.

One of the smaller children was pushed to the back in the scramble and seeing this Marina picked her up and pushed her way to the front, before retiring to an area at the back, where the only competition was with the school cat. Walter saw what had happened and intrigued he made his way through the children to where Marina was standing. He asked a number of questions and Marina replied courteously and immediately they liked each other.

Marina had acquired a great deal of wisdom for one so young and her experiences had made her astute beyond her years and her remarkable gift for assessing character satisfied her that Walter Smith was genuine.

It was a short conversation, which ended reluctantly on both sides by the sound of the school bell. Marina made her apologies and left for the big door, which led to the main hall. She turned and watched Walter disappear out of sight into the Principal's office which was situated in a building nearby and she wondered whether she would see him again until a voice assured her that she would. There was no one there but Marina did not feel the need to investigate why.

The following week Marina was sitting alone in a classroom when the caretaker walked silently through the open door. She was looking out of the window whilst the rain cascaded against the paved area outside. As the caretaker drew near Marina heard what she thought was a warning shout from someone in the distance. Startled, she stepped back as the visitor moved closer towards her. He was offering a small packet of sweets but there was something about his manner and his eyes in particular that made her move away, despite his token assurances.

Marina turned and ran outside and to sanctuary in the chapel and when the door was closed she breathed a sigh of relief for she had seen that look before on the face of Heung. She had been protected by the warning from her spiritual friend who was becoming a constant visitor at times of isolation.

This particular workman was the talk of the older girls who constantly referred to him in private discussions as the man with the wandering hands. Whenever he appeared a shiver ran up Marina's spine and the feeling of hatred and disgust returned to haunt her.

Walter became a regular visitor to the Home, spending more time on each visit with the children and the staff. He had taken a liking to Marina, and took a great deal of interest in her case. He was made aware of her background and the terrible trauma which she had suffered which prompted him to discuss the prospects of adoption with his wife. It was true that he had wished to balance the family unit by adopting a baby boy, and Marina was over twelve years old, but Walter was a very spiritual man with a considerable concern for the common good and the more he saw of Marina, the more he liked her. On each of his visits they took to having long discussions in the school playing field on many subjects, but Walter left the question of adoption well alone.

If Marina really wanted to be adopted and live in a nice home, she had a peculiar way of going about it because whenever those conversations with Walter took place she was always pushing the younger ones forward, giving them preference. Walter was intrigued that one so young, who had suffered so much would place the consideration of others before herself, but he was quite convinced that she was genuine.

On one such visit, Walter decided that he would offer Marina a home. He had discussed the possibility with the authorities who had satisfied themselves as to Walter's character and raised no objection to the adoption process. The next hurdle was to solicit Marina's view.

It was one lovely summer afternoon at the house and there was a garden party held on the lawn. There were lots of bring and buy stalls and competitions for the children. Tables were bedecked with bright cloths and were crammed with every assortment of sandwich and cake imaginable. There were jugs of iced water and soda pop and an unusual but refreshing concoction called Dandelion and Burdock which proved popular with the guests. The children wore their very best clothes and there was considerable excitement in the air as groups of small children scurried around the stalls laughing and shouting whilst some of the older ones delivered drinks and carried out other tasks.

Walter visited the various stalls, bought raffle tickets and was handed in sequence a number of glasses of Dandelion and Burdock until he caught sight of his favourite child. Marina brought him a glass of Dandelion and Burdock and they laughed in unison when she discovered a tray in his other hand containing five other glasses. She then passed him a sandwich and then a cake only to laugh again when she saw four such plates resting on the coffee table beside him. Marina then brought out a pack of raffle tickets only to find that he was carrying at least thirty concealed in each of his jacket pockets.

They walked around the various stalls until they arrived at the coconut shy where Walter removed his jacket, took up three wooden balls and threw them with such velocity that the third one caught the row of coconuts to send them tumbling to the floor. Marina squealed with delight as the stallholder handed over a small teddy bear as a prize. It was new and undamaged.

After the tour was complete they sat on the grass near to the old greenhouse on the back lawn and talked about the Home. During the conversation Marina became aware of a whispered voice but as she looked around she could not see anyone, and yet the voice continued with the words, 'this is the one'. Walter realised that her attention had been distracted but when he queried what had happened Marina passed it off without explanation.

Walter was finding it difficult to broach the situation until he took a deep breath and asked Marina if she would like to join his family. It was a strange but most sincere way of putting it by a man who found it difficult to wear his heart on his sleeve.

Marina did not reply but the look on her face gave away her feelings and her answer and so later that afternoon Walter met with the Principal to give him the news.

The next three months were spent making preparations, which included numerous visits to Walter's home. Marina's favourite visit was to the family fish and chip shop where she would enjoy her own serving of fishcake and chips with the wonderful addition of chip shop vinegar.

Marina's first meeting with Walter's daughter Shirley was a concern for them both. The relationship had to work in the entire family but there would always be the fear that the very best of intentions might not work and so the home visits went on for some time with Marina staying overnight on a regular basis. Everyone tried their best and she fitted in well, so much so that they all agreed with the adoption process.

The day of Marina's departure soon arrived and that morning she was up early. Her packing was soon complete and once again Marina was to start a different chapter in her life in a new home with a new family, but there was much sadness upon her departure.

The other children gathered at the front doors in friendly salute as Marina greeted Walter, Edna and Shirley. They walked hand in hand to the car and Marina sat in the front with Walter. Walter was desperately keen to give Marina a new life and consequently he decided that it would start with a change of name. From the date of the adoption she became known as Patricia Smith, and for the first time in her life she felt truly special.

As the car drove off Patricia looked straight ahead; she did not permit herself a backward glance.

INTO HAPPINESS

The transition from the streets of Kowloon to the children's home and then to the Smith's house was nothing less than remarkable. In her short life Trisha as she became known had lived with families who observed different religions. There was Catholicism in the convent and Buddhism in Hong Kong, and then she moved to live with Walter Smith who was a Mormon and his wife a member of The Salvation Army. He was a very kind and generous man and seeing the extent of Marina's wardrobe he bought new dresses for her. There was one dress which she liked more than the others which was white with small red cherries all over and a huge red bow wrapped around the waist. Walter commented that Trisha looked like a princess when she wore it and often called her by that name. After the dowdy convent dress, Chinese clothes and hand-me-downs in Dr Barnardos, the new wardrobe was a welcome change.

Walter had spent a great deal of his life working for charitable causes and his influence upon the family unit and those around him prompted great respect and loyalty. His career in the Royal Air Force had enabled him to travel extensively, and on his various excursions abroad he brought back gifts for the whole family. Trisha missed her new father during his absences but the delight at his return was all the more worthwhile, particularly when the presents were handed out. There were the finest silks from India, dolls from Russia, and presents from Africa, but nothing could compare with his return and the weekend trips to the swimming baths and the park, and the wonderful picnics they shared.

Trisha tried to form a good relationship with Shirley but she was an only child and averse to allowing a new member into the family.

She had found happiness with her new parents and the voices had stopped, for she had no need of support and company, but one day when she was sitting in the garden a familiar sound came to her ears. It was as if it was a warning, but the tone of the voice was strange and guarded, unlike anything she had heard before, but she dismissed the thought from her head as she returned to the house

The family home was spacious and had a large garden, not unlike that at the big house in Hong Kong. There was a large swing at the top of the garden, bordered by large conifer trees, which gave off a wonderful scent when dashed with rainwater. Trisha would sit and play on the swing in quiet contemplation, during which time the voices visited her again.

Her new school was close at hand, only a matter of a few minutes walk from home and although there had been a substantial break in her schooling whilst in Hong Kong she soon caught up, utilising her exceptional memory in the process. Her relationship with the other pupils was excellent, but tragically this rather idyllic existence was not to last.

Walter had been given an assignment overseas, which was to take him to Burma which would mean that he was to be away from home for some months and unfortunately would miss the Christmas festivities. On the day that the letter was received Trisha was playing on the swing. She knew of and expected the communication before it arrived, having been told of it in one of her contemplative moments on the swing. She went into the house and watched intently as Walter opened the official looking letter and as he discarded the envelope Trisha could see the initials RAF printed near the postmark.

Walter seemed more interested than pleased and he called Edna and the children to his side and told them that it was a good opportunity and whilst they would have to stay at home, it would not be long before he returned. It was particularly disappointing for the children because his absence would coincide with the annual school Christmas holidays.

Trisha forced a smile as he spoke of the wonderful presents which would herald his return, but something plagued her mind with great foreboding.

She spent a considerable amount of time with Walter during the six weeks prior to his departure and their relationship became stronger than ever. Trisha had found the father figure she had been searching for and Walter, the second child for whom he yearned, but at the back of her mind was the nagging doubt that it would not and could not last.

Departure day came all too quickly and that morning Trisha was sitting on the swing staring into space when once again she heard a voice. It was the same whisper that came to her in the Home, but this time it did not bring good tidings.

In her own small way she tried to dissuade Walter from going, but she knew that her intervention might be seen to be motivated by personal gain. She even declined to help him pack his suitcases, something which aroused his concern as he had realised that Trisha had an insight into events happening around her. He had noted on a number of occasions that she had made minor predictions, which generally speaking came true, which prompted him to tell her that she was 'special'. No one will ever know what Walter thought or believed although he often spoke of an afterlife and 'guardian angels'. Whatever it was he accepted Trisha's gift with good grace and never tried to dissuade her from using it.

The family accompanied Walter to the airport, which brought back unhappy memories as Trisha entered the visitors' departure area. Walter said his farewells and Trisha was overcome with the feeling that she was seeing him for the last time. She held him tightly making it necessary for Walter to free himself when his flight number was called.

It was a moving scene as Walter walked into passport control and as he waved to his family his eyes caught Trisha's, and for a second he appeared to realise her concern. He faltered for a moment before smiling and waving again and then he blew a kiss to the three of them in turn before disappearing amongst a large group of people busily queuing to enter the departure lounge.

Trisha watched as the plane soared into the sky and she squinted as she watched its flight path head towards the sun. It was an eerie and unforgettable moment.

Letters were received regularly and on Sundays Walter would telephone home at precisely 6pm GMT. The conversations were generally the same with an exchange of good wishes and comments of regret at his absence. With the majority of the relatively short call spent between Edna and himself, Walter spoke to each of his family without exception before ringing off until the next time.

The rest of the winter holiday was spent at play, although Trisha had taken to spending more and more of her time alone during which time the voices returned, stronger and more persistent than before. She acquired a remarkable knack of being able to predict people's health problems, which was a never-ending source of fun and amusement to the family and friends. She had also taken to spending time playing cards not in the sense of games but in a peculiar fashion, which led to her telling her friends of hidden meanings when the cards were displayed in a particular sequence. One Sunday she had been playing on the swing when she realised that Edna and Shirley were in the hallway, waiting for the telephone to ring. On this occasion she remained swinging so furiously that the seat was almost level with the supporting crossbar. Her eyes were staring as if transfixed by some apparition, until Edna disturbed her.

When she entered the house Edna and Shirley were sitting staring at the telephone. Somehow she knew that something had happened. 6pm came and went but there was no call and it was not until the following evening that the telephone finally rang and someone from the RAF told Edna that Walter had been taken ill and owing to the limited facilities at his base he had been taken to the local hospital. At first they were told that he had a fever and it would be a matter of a few days before he would be able to contact home, but the caller promised to keep the family informed. Edna put down the telephone without saying a word; her face told the story. Shirley started to cry and Edna tried to comfort her but Trisha ran out into the garden and looked into the sky as if seeking inspiration whereupon she sank to her knees; she was inconsolable.

On Christmas Eve Trisha and Shirley spent the day trimming up the Christmas tree. It was over seven feet high and used up all the available baubles which the Smiths had saved over the years. Walter's absence had placed a damp blanket over the proceedings, although Shirley was determined to enjoy the festivities for her father's sake but Trisha on the other hand was unusually morose. Edna was busy in the kitchen preparing food for the following day, but theirs was to be a quiet Christmas spent at home watching television and playing with the many gifts which Walter had bought for them all.

There was no excitement about the following day and all three of them were subdued. Edna was in the kitchen and Shirley was playing with one of the Christmas presents whilst Trisha was staring into the television seemingly listening intently to the programme, until her attention focused on the Christmas tree and its lights as they flashed on and off in quick succession, and then she was overcome by a great sadness.

It was just after 3pm when the police called. There was a hard knocking on the door which made Edna jump and Trisha's heart sank. Her body felt drained of life and in expectation of bad tidings.

The officer who called was a fresh-faced young man with curly ginger hair. He had bright eyes and a fresh complexion and Trisha noted two marks on his cheek where over-industrious shaving had resulted in two very minor wounds. He was tall and even gangly, although his head was bowed betraying his true height. He remained in the hallway, but within a matter of seconds he had gone, having carried out his grim duty, his offer of service being politely declined.

Edna sank to her knees and Shirley held her tightly. The old feelings of trauma and insecurity returned to haunt Trisha. She too fell to her knees and all three joined in a seemingly never-ending embrace.

Walter died on Christmas Day of double pneumonia and Trisha was always to associate that day with the death of her beloved Walter.

The responsibility for the funeral arrangements fell upon Edna and perhaps understandably she was having a great deal of difficulty in dealing with all the various problems which this caused. The Royal Air Force were very helpful and a representative called to see her and helped her as best he could, but there were difficulties in fixing the date of the funeral, because the death had occurred overseas.

It was approximately three weeks before the authorities would release the body.

There was just a hint of snow in the air on the morning of the funeral and the assembled group of family and friends shivered as they walked up the driveway. A variety of cars arrived and the guests left for the church whilst Trisha and Shirley stayed at home with a neighbour to look after them. Shirley remained in her room and despite the weather Trisha went out to her swing. She did not feel the cold. The brilliant illusion of at last having a father of her own had been torn away from her. She felt that her soul has been destroyed once more.

She was still on the swing when the guests returned. There were muffled voices as a selected buffet was handed around to reluctant diners whilst Trisha remained outside despite assurances from well-intentioned mourners. Tired faces reacted to the solemnity of the occasion which suppressed any interaction between the visitors who were sitting uncomfortably on the available chairs throughout the house.

Trisha listened as various visitors passed comment about the service and the efforts of the undertaker and other superfluous comment. Perhaps understandably everyone avoided any mention of Walter in a genuine attempt to prevent causing distress, but it served only to create an entirely artificial situation, broken only by a constant stream of people making their apologies and leaving.

Inevitably there were comparisons between Trisha, Shirley and their mother by the other mourners. There is something strangely compelling about observing those in distress, but on this occasion it was borne out of genuine concern as opposed to morbid curiosity.

Eventually the visitors started to drift away when they felt it was appropriate to do so, until the only people left were Edna and the children and the ageing aunt Edith (Walter's sister) who had fallen asleep.

Trisha overheard a conversation between Edna and Aunt Edith, who had always resented her presence. Aunt Edith expressed her concern as to whether or not Edna would be able to cope with the remorse, the business and the two girls, suggesting that perhaps Patricia should be sent back to Dr Barnados. Edna refuted the suggestion by saying that she was prepared to work hard for as long as she could and be responsible for her two daughters.

Edna was tired and quickly retired to bed, but Trisha remained downstairs clearing away. There was no conversation; it just did not seem appropriate. Eventually both girls went upstairs but Trisha was unable to find sleep which left her waiting and watching for the sunrise, as once more the experience of grief had returned to haunt her.

Over the next few weeks Edna's mental stability began to waiver. She was morose and given to outbursts of crying, prompted by her belief that she was in some way to blame for Walter's death. She was unable to venture out of the house even to visit the shops and consequently she became even more unhappy and depressed.

In the meantime and not for the first time in her short life, Trisha was left to her own devices in a mirror image of the turn of events in Hong Kong following Mr Chan's death. Trisha was in a most vulnerable position for she was unable to rely on Edna for support as she had become unpredictable.

During the last week of the following January there was an incident which was to change the complexion of the relationship and family unit even further.   Trisha and Shirley were compiling schoolwork in one of the upstairs bedrooms believing that Edna was busy in the kitchen ostensibly preparing the evening meal.

Trisha was alerted by the pungent smell of gas rising into the bedroom, which prompted the two girls to run downstairs.   Fortunately a passer-by alerted the police and a burly police officer threw some object to smash the window and then forced his way in.   The girls were taken outside as the officer searched for Edna and the source of the supply.   He found all of the rings on the cooker turned on and all the windows and doors closed. Edna was found sitting on the kitchen floor as if in a daze.   The only explanation was that she had attempted suicide.   The air vents in the room had been blocked with tissues and stockings ensuring that fresh air could not enter the house and no gas could escape.

The police officer had saved the family from a gruesome fate, at a time when the balance of Edna's mind was clearly disturbed.   She was hospitalised and saw a variety of doctors before she was eventually allowed home.   Walter's death had taken its toll and she had suffered a nervous breakdown.

Unfortunately, the years were not kind to Edna, although she sought solace in a friendship with the police officer who saved her life that day. He was a frequent visitor to the house and a relationship developed. Eventually he moved in with her but so far as Trisha was concerned he was no replacement for Walter and eventually relations within the family unit broke down, which prompted her to confide her thoughts to Edna's brother Ivor who lived with his wife Maisie near Nottingham. Over the years she got on very well with Ivor and Maisie and knowing of her unhappiness they began to let her stay with them at weekends. Eventually her visits extended to the whole of the school holidays and then, when she reached the age of fifteen she ran away from home and moved in with them on a permanent basis, although she still had contact with Edna by telephone and enjoyed the occasional visit. She was happy with Ivor's family who encouraged her in relation to her remarkable ability to communicate with spirits from the past, which brought comfort and solace to them all.

When she was almost sixteen and after disguising her true age, Trisha consulted a Medium called Mrs Bullock. She was curious and wanted a reading, wondering what destiny had in store for her. When Trisha entered the room Mrs Bullock said that she felt a psychic presence. She predicted that when Trisha reached her late thirties she would achieve great success as a Medium, comforting and helping people along the way. She further predicted that she would stand on a circular stage wearing silver shoes and conduct a demonstration, relaying messages from the spirit world to a large audience. The prediction could not have influenced Trisha's life because she wanted to be a nurse and clairvoyance was the furthest thing from her mind.

WOMANHOOD

E venings at Ivor's were a friendly affair. They were nice easygoing people who had originated from Ebbw Vale in Wales where strong family relationships were a feature of community life. Saturday evenings were usually spent around the fireside where Trisha held centre stage telling an enthralled audience of family and friends of the voices who continually came to her. She had become quite adept at being able to translate symbols into messages from the spirit world and there was no hiding this remarkable talent and with the encouragement that Ivor and his wife gave her she was able to develop this wonderful gift. She was no longer chastised or ridiculed or made to feel guilty and consequently the voices came to her more easily.

She began to visit the library and read books on spiritualism to try to obtain a greater understanding of the subject and relate the information she was receiving to her special gift which led to a greater realisation of what the spirit world was trying to say. Regular meditation enhanced her spirituality and she became adept at clairvoyance, the ability to see events either in the past, present or future which would take the form of visions like an impression of a photograph or in motion, similar to a video recording.

This insight was supported by clairaudience, which is the ability to hear spirit voices and communicate messages exactly as they are given from the spirit world.

Eventually she was able to read the life record of inanimate objects, a form of clairvoyance because psychic vision is able to impart knowledge of individuals from the object provided.

There can be no doubt that she was extremely advanced for her age and doubtless her life experiences had propelled her into womanhood much earlier than would normally have been the case. When she left school she made herself busy for a few pounds here and there giving readings to interested parties who had sought her out. She acquired her own flat and began to build her own home and although she kept in constant touch with Ivor it was a time for advancement and individuality and Trisha seized her opportunity with both hands.

Despite all that Trisha had suffered in her life she had never lost her faith and she started to attend the Spiritualist churches on a regular basis. Followers of the belief were impressed with her insight and she was invited to visit different venues in the locality and to speak and utilise her gifts. Albeit within a small circle she became well-known, with the result that she was asked to give more and more readings to an ever interested and sometimes enthralled public.

Her home conditions improved and she was proud of her flat which was a simple dwelling with two living rooms, three bedrooms and the usual facilities. The walls and ledges were bedecked with religious memorabilia and pictures of religious scenes and in pride of place over a sculpture of two hands praying was a sort of rosary with a crucifix which Marina had given to her all those years before and which accompanied Trisha everywhere she went. It was, and still is, very precious to her.

When she was seventeen Trisha met a local man who was much older than her but handsome and with a sense of humour that made her laugh. They became firm friends and eventually, spurred on by the impatience of youth, he moved into the flat and her first love affair began.

Arrangements were made for a wedding and here it seemed Trisha had found the true happiness that she had yearned for; the question was, for how long would it last.

Despite an earlier medical prognosis that she was unable to conceive, Trisha's happiness was complete when she became pregnant with twins. Her partner was delighted and together they made plans for the forthcoming births and started to look at larger accommodation which would be suitable for a family of four. But then one day in February fate once more played its cruel hand. Trisha had a premonition; similar to the one she experienced when Walter died. It left her feeling unhappy and unwell, such was her sensitivity to the experience.

Her partner was travelling to the East Coast in his car on business. It was a bright sunny day without the hint of a breeze. The warm air entered the car through an open window and he sat comfortably enjoying the drive and the passing countryside as he travelled along a narrow country road. The only other vehicle in the vicinity was a lorry in the distance and which was travelling towards him.

The circumstances were somewhat confused, but later that day Trisha received a message from the police that was to turn her world upside-down once again. There had been a collision and he had been killed instantly.

It is difficult to begin to understand how she must have felt as once more she was haunted by the spectres of grief and despair but she had her faith and the prospect of the twins, but nothing more.

A cynic would suggest that Trisha should have foreseen what was to happen but the answer would be that she had not. Thankfully it is not always possible for a Medium to see into the future for herself; such a burden would be too much of a cross for a mere mortal to bear.

Not surprisingly Trisha was ill during the pregnancy, and two months later, on March 24th Kelly her daughter was born prematurely at a weight of only four pounds and two ounces. The other baby, a boy, was stillborn. When she was well enough to leave hospital she returned to her flat to be cared for by a neighbour, an old lady called Mrs Bird, until Trisha was able to look after herself. Desperate for money she started to organise readings, which helped her to eke out a living and provide as best she could for her child. It was a lonely existence, but she had the spirit world for company in the evenings when she sat alone with her thoughts.

As time passed by she acquired a clientele as her name was passed around sympathisers in the area, and her days were shared between her clients and her daughter.

On one occasion about a year after her partner's death, she was walking in the park with Kelly in her pram when she met Peter. His relationship with his wife had broken-up and he had taken a walk to reflect upon his future. A chance conversation made Trisha laugh for the first time in over a year. Fate decreed that this would not be their last meeting.

The following week Trisha was taking her usual walk when quite by chance she met Peter again. Their conversation lasted for the whole of the afternoon and inevitably the association developed with the result that just under a year later Peter moved into the flat. Trisha accepted his proposal of marriage and during this time she conceived a child. Her son Lee was born on 16th March 1984 and later that year Trisha was married, and Peter took over the role of father to Kelly.

He was a good worker and provider for the family, but unfortunately their happiness was not to last. Eventually after seven years of marriage they separated and thereafter they were divorced. Once more Trisha was alone, but this time there were two children and so once again she returned to readings to keep the fabric of the family unit intact.

It was a period in her life which is best described as the wilderness years. And so we move on to 1986 when Trisha met Jane.

JANE

Trisha met Jane Thorpe in 1986. Jane had visited Trisha's house with a group of friends for readings. The reality of the situation was that Jane had been co-opted into the group to make up the numbers but during the meeting Trisha had looked at Jane's aura and she saw a grey area surrounding one of her breasts. To Jane's astonishment Trisha told her that she believed she had visualised a lump and advised her to seek medical treatment the very next day.

Shortly after that meeting, Jane was diagnosed with cancer, but the prognosis was good for the hospital had caught the condition in its infancy and was able to treat it.

After the treatment was complete Jane went to see Trisha again for a reading. The appointment was due to take one hour but it lasted all afternoon and by the end of it they were firm friends. Theirs was a remarkable bonding which made them soulmates, forging a friendship which lasted until the end of Jane's life.

They met regularly. They went out together, stayed in together, went shopping, shared meals and concerns about their respective children. It was a wonderful relationship that benefited them both. If they did not meet every day they would speak on the telephone and sometimes they would do both. Jane was popular with Trisha's children who treated her as a favourite aunt, enjoying her visits and her company. Jane also benefited by extending her family circle to include them. She had a son of her own who was younger than Kelly and older than Lee, but he too was accepted into the greater family and brought further joy to the unit. Jane and Trisha were both single parents and Geminis, thus sharing an empathy with each other.

Towards the end of the eighties Trisha met Jeff, a man ten years her senior and a financial consultant with whom she formed a relationship. To all intents and purposes she had everything, her work, her beliefs, a relationship, two children and a friendship which would stand the test of time.

It was an idyllic situation, perhaps too good to last, but the all too familiar equation heralded fate's cruel interference.

In 1986 Jane's cancer returned and after considerable testing it was found that the disease had travelled to the brain. The prognosis was inevitable and despite the valiant efforts of the hospital, tragically it was too late.

Trisha and Jane spent hours discussing the possibilities before deciding that they would not give up hope. Perhaps they had to hang onto something and so a mutual deception took place, doubtless in an attempt to ease the inevitability of Jane's passing.

During Jane's hospitalisation she became very spiritual and she did not fear death but found solace in her belief that she was destined for a better place. Throughout her illness Jane was a very courageous person, and this unselfish behaviour was an inspiration not only to her family and Trisha but to everyone with whom she had contact.

Towards the end, Trisha visited her every day and on one occasion Jane spoke to her with a knowledge and an understanding which she had not been heard before. It was as if Jane had been given a second sight and for once the roles were reversed and Trisha had become the subject of a reading.

Jane also told Trisha that one day she would give readings at theatres throughout the country and abroad saying that she would wear silver shoes and audiences would come in numbers to hear her, but this achievement would not be made alone. It was then that Jane made a startling prophecy. She said that Trisha would meet a man just over fifty years of age with hair turning grey. He would be born of the Twins (Gemini), have the initials 'S' and when they met she would realise his identity because he would be writing a book about a famous man. It was a peculiar prophecy, but the memory of it was to live in Trisha's memory until events were to remind her of it some time later.

Jane was anxious to return home and accordingly the hospital honoured her wishes and she was allowed to leave, to be visited daily by one of the specialist nurses. She suffered greatly but her mind remained clear and focused. Her thoughts were for her family and friends and there were many, such was her popularity.

The weather on the day of Trisha's last visit was warm, with a gentle breeze which wafted the branches of trees heavily-laden with large buds ready to burst into leaf when the time was right. Trisha entered the house and felt a chill as she climbed the stairs to Jane's bedroom.

Jane's tortured face managed a smile as Trisha moved towards the bed. The two friends held each other gently, for Jane was in so much pain that the drugs had seemed to lose their potency. She knew her time had come, and so did Trisha.

They talked about their children and then the conversation turned to Trisha's future. Once again she was reminded of the prophecy, but at that time it made little sense to her, but nevertheless she promised that one day she would wear the silver shoes and one day they would meet again in a better place.

When the conversation ended Jane was tired and said she wanted to sleep. It was her way of alleviating the necessity of Trisha having to witness her death. Before Trisha left, she kissed Jane on the cheek and told her that she loved her very much. Jane opened her eyes, took Trisha's hand and squeezed it with such force that Trisha was made to wince. She then smiled, closed her eyes and took a deep breath; it was her last. With it went all the pain and the suffering.

Despite realising the inevitable, Trisha was broken-hearted. The friend who never judged her, made demands or criticised her had gone and once more Trisha was left isolated and in despair. Jane was just fifty-one years of age.

Fortunately Trisha had her faith which helped to moderate the numbing sensation of loss and with time the inevitable healer spurred on by her promise to Jane that she would seek the silver shoes, she continued with her readings from a small office near to where she lived. Kelly left school and started work, but Lee maintained his interest in education and began to forge a considerable expertise in sport. Trisha's friend Jeff had a good relationship with the children and introduced Lee to the local tennis scene where his talent was encouraged to attain a high standard.

Financially things were a struggle and ensuring that her children were well provided for Trisha neglected herself and from time to time her health would suffer. She continued to appear at Spiritualist Churches and at various halls and theatres in the area which gave her a measure of localised celebrity status, providing a grounding and experience upon which she would rely in the future when greater tasks challenged her and with love, courage and faith she would continue her spiritual work.

PART TWO

MY FIRST APPEARANCE

I made my first appearance in this story in June 1997 when Trisha and I met for the first time. The previous year I had been harbouring feelings of dissatisfaction and confusion amidst inexplicable restlessness in my search for something new. I had taken up Reiki and dabbled with Reflexology with the idea of pushing back the adversities of time, which had brought to me bad knees and a back prone to aching if it was subjected to heavy lifting.

I was working hard trying to run a legal office with nearly thirty staff whilst jousting with the problems that only the bank and VAT inspectors can bring. My limited leisure time had been taken up writing the biography of the famous black Yorkshire comedian Charlie Williams but the totality of the situation created a heavy and burdensome series of undertakings which had begun to take their toll. I tried many things to combat fatigue, from multi-vitamins to food supplements to early nights, none of which proved successful, but then I was introduced to Reiki.

Reiki is a hands-on technique in which the therapist radiates concentrated life-force energy, or the 'Ki' as it is known, which action stimulates the bodies own natural healing abilities, resulting in a deeply relaxing experience during which the therapist gently places his or her hands over a series of positions on the head and body of the subject.

I found Reiki relaxing and it opened my mind to a new philosophy, which led to a time for decisions, but above all it introduced me to Spiritualism.

As a result I had also taken to reading about the subject, which had been prompted by a desire to find a direction different from the one that I had been following and the need to find answers to so many of life's mysteries. It was that search which introduced me to a number of Mediums whom I hoped would help with the information I was seeking. One Medium in particular stood out in my mind; an individual who had described seeing a book with the pages all blank which would enjoy success at some time or other. My first thoughts were of Charlie's book, but it was half finished and consequently not all the pages would be blank so I realised that he must have seen something else – but what?

I chose not to dwell on the prophecy and continued with my life, much as it had been before, but my fascination for the subject of Spiritualism opened up another avenue when I was given the name of a woman called Trisha, a Medium much in demand and highly commended. The subsequent meeting between us was to change our lives forever.

After a number of conversations with an answerphone I managed to speak with her and made an appointment which was subsequently cancelled, as was the second, until on the third occasion we actually met.

I drove down the A1 to Ollerton, and found a village of two halves, with the older part forming a picturesque area more properly to be expected of a 1950's setting. I made my way past the church and the village pub, to arrive at the centre point after rounding a corner. It was a warm and languid June day which served to enhance the first picture I had of this quaint area. The smell of freshly-cut hay permeated the street as it floated on the warm air to greet me on the way to her office.

We had not met before and consequently neither of us knew who to look for, but as I walked round the corner which led to her office I became aware of a young woman walking towards me. I had the compulsion to smile in greeting, something which was returned as she drew close. For some reason we realised who the other was although as I remember it neither gave the appearance of being lost nor of looking for anyone.

The woman spoke using my name and I replied having realised who she was. My years in the legal profession had taught me to sum up personalities on a first meeting and as I went through the motions I was immediately struck by her smartly dressed appearance, with her dark, alert eyes and auburn coloured hair. We shook hands and exchanged pleasantries before I was taken to an office on the High Street opposite the church.

We entered a rather interesting room possessed of a peaceful serenity. It housed a settee and some unusual pictures of American Red Indians on the walls. There were intriguing artefacts and items of religious memorabilia situated in most of the nooks and crannies around the walls, whilst on the table next to where Trisha was sitting was a large brass crucifix standing resplendent on an oak plinth. The room was dimly lit, but I felt comfortable and substantially at ease.

As the meeting began I was aware that Trisha was studying me; looking around the framework of my body as if I was encased in some form of sarcophagus. I was surprised to be told that I had been treated for ulcers and had suffered an operation to my right knee at some time in the recent past. She was of course correct on both counts but before I could reflect upon how she could have known such facts, she began to tell me other things from my past.

I wanted to know where this information came from, but I was too busy listening to interrupt and as I had no wish to break her concentration, I merely sat listening and responded only if a comment was required.

I was most impressed after she had offered some general information, and even more so when she told me that a spirit was actually with me in the room. She told me that he was a relatively young man recently taken into the spirit world and I was intrigued because I knew of such a person. I was frustrated by my lack of knowledge of the subject, for whilst I was able to take in what she was saying, I was baffled as to how this information seemed to be so freely available.

She told me that the spirit had just attained fifty years on earth but had passed on to the spirit world following problems with his stomach. She said that she could visualise the spirit pointing to his abdominal area highlighting the scene of the problem. Trisha told me that he had wanted to thank me for my kindness at the time of his illness, although a measure of modesty had prevented me from accepting such a plaudit, but then came the bombshell when she actually gave me my friend's Christian name.

Keith Clayton had been a friend of mine for over twenty-five years and I had worked with him for a period of ten of those years. In the latter part of 1998 however he had been diagnosed as suffering from stomach cancer and unfortunately the problem had gone too far and was inoperable. Keith knew he was dying but he did not know when.

My last meeting with Keith was at a rather expensive restaurant in the west of Yorkshire where we enjoyed a wonderful meal in most pleasant and acceptable surroundings, consuming an incredible amount of drink in the process. Understandably Keith was pre-occupied but inevitably the conversation moved around to his illness and the plans he had made for his family. Keith was to drive home after the meal and I remember pointing out that he must have been well and truly over the legal limit, but he smiled and pointed out that a long disqualification would not possibly concern him. We had arranged to meet again two weeks later, but the night before the appointment Keith was taken into hospital and he most regrettably passed over the following night.

It was the most remarkable luncheon appointment of my life but despite the rather solemn nature of what was to be our final meeting I felt at ease, with no feeling of embarrassment.

Trisha told me of the arrangement and of Keith's inability to attend our meeting because of his hospitalisation.

She told me that Keith had 'spoken' to her and he wanted me to know he was happy and contented now that his problems were over. This information sent my mind racing. How did she know about Keith and the details of his death unless she had actually spoken to him? Trisha told me that she was going to put forward proof that Keith was actually there and promptly suggested that he wanted to give me a sign as evidence. Whenever Keith and I met we had formed the habit of saluting each other. Trisha could not have understood the reason or meaning behind this but nevertheless she stood in front of me and told me that she knew I would understand. She then gave the salute in exactly the same way as Keith used to perform it and I have to admit that my breath was taken away.

I cast my mind back to seeing fortune-tellers in the past and realised that they were extremely perceptive with remarkable powers of deduction, but the information given to me was not capable of being deduced for I had not told her anything. I had neither said nor done anything to give any clue upon which such conclusions could have been based.

The jigsaw was complete when she gave me his first name and of course she was right. The only explanation was that she must have had some insight, but from where?

The rest of the reading comprised general information during which time she gave me the names of two of my closest friends and described their employment and the nature of our relationships, before turning to some obscure detail about my three dogs. One of them had an injured ear, or so she said, but at the time I knew of no such injury but she argued the point so forcefully that I just accepted what she had said. She also told me that a friend of mine called Tom would call to see me 'with tears' but I was still reeling as a result of the message from Keith so that I did not place too much significance upon it. But the very best was saved until last.

One spirit made contact and I was told that he was a relative. Trisha spoke of an old man, huge in stature with a handlebar moustache but I could not place him and so further clues were revealed to me; for example he was a pipe-smoker and Trisha said that she could actually sense the smell of the tobacco which she described as having a pungent aroma. Apparently she could visualise him with the pipe dangling out of the corner of his mouth with the mouthpiece engulfed with saliva which spread on to his facial hair. I was still unable to grasp who he could have been and so she gave me further clues including the information that he worked on the fish-trawling boats in Grimsby, but still I was unable to recognise him. The final attempt to identify him was made by her supplying his two Christian names of John and Thomas, but it meant nothing, although Trisha explained that whilst he was a relative he could have been an old spirit from way back in the past.

I assumed that for once she had simply made a mistake but in the light of all the wondrous things which I had been told I thought the least I could do would be to allow her one error.

When I returned home my mother was waiting for me to tell me of two incidents which had happened that day. My bitch dog Georgie had been taken to the vet because she had torn one of her ears on some barbed wire. This rather astonishing news was a mere preamble to something far more interesting.

My mother also told me that a friend of mine from the locality called Tom had called to cancel an arrangement we had for a visit to an Italian restaurant because Tom's father-in-law had died earlier that morning. I could not help but repeat Trisha's words under my breath – 'Tom will come 'with tears'' – and so I set about telling my mother about this remarkable meeting and what I had been told.

When I had finished my story I thought it only right to 'balance the books' by relating the one and only error which I believed she had made.

I began as Trisha had by explaining that the spirit who she said had come was an old man, huge in stature with a handlebar moustache. As I related the story I watched my mother intently to see if there was any sign of recognition but alas there was none. It was a fair conclusion that if she did not recognise the so-called member of my family from the past, then no one would, but I persevered because of the persistence with which she had relayed the message. I told her that she had been most specific about the aroma of pipe tobacco and then I noticed that the reference to the evil-smelling mixture had struck a chord.

My mother explained that she recalled her own grandfather as being a large man who smoked a foul-smelling tobacco but she said that he did not actually smoke a pipe in the traditional way. She told me how the pipe used to dangle from the corner of his mouth and all the family would be appalled at the state of the saliva-covered item as it dangled from the side of his face. This small, obscure and yet vital piece of information left me staggered but before I could speak my mother continued to tell me that great grandfather was a considerable character who used to work on the trawlers out of Grimsby. Before she could continue I interrupted by asking if his Christian names were John and Thomas. This disclosure stopped my mother in her tracks and she asked me how I knew his name and for a moment we were both dumbfounded. Whether perceptive or not, how on earth would Trisha have been able to state those facts? It was certainly nothing she could have deduced from anything I had said because I didn't recognise who she was talking about but the enormity and the importance of what I had been told really registered with me.

The following day I was performing the ritual of emptying my suit so that my pens, diary and other documents would be available for the next day, when I came across four tickets which Trisha had given me for the forthcoming performance at The Palace Theatre at Retford. It was inevitable that I would turn up as my search for truth and understanding had just begun. I telephoned her and she was delighted to hear that I was going to attend, particularly when I confirmed the identity of the man with the handlebar moustache.

Four weeks later I attended the Theatre, and if I had thought that my initial meeting with her was something of an eye-opener, further remarkable confirmation was on its way.

The Palace Theatre at Retford had been in the hands of an enthusiastic team of voluntary workers whose hard work and dedication managed to re-open the Theatre and make it viable. This wonderful group of people had taken to hiring out the Theatre to a number of users who used it for their own purposes. It was also a convenient vehicle for Trisha to bring her message to a wider audience.

It was a pleasant warm July evening as I drove around the same Retford streets trying to find the Theatre which had been hidden from view by development but eventually I found it and managed to get there with only seconds to spare before the performance began. I sat in a seat some eight to ten rows back from the stage, close enough to see a number of devotees waiting anxiously in the hope that they would be chosen to receive a message. Some interesting and rather peaceful music played through the speakers at the side of the stage and the lighting was dimmed to give an almost surreal effect to the proceedings.

I had never been to a Medium's exhibition before but I found a strange affinity for the subject, with no fear or concern, but there was a curiosity and an excitement which I had not felt before.

The audience were predominantly female but the age group varied from teenage girls giggling excitedly to aged persons speaking in whispers. There was a buzz of excitement before the proceedings commenced and I could hear one couple in front of me talking about previous events and some of the remarkable stories which Trisha had told.

Whilst I knew and accepted that there was some strange almost mystical power, I was not fully converted into the religious aspect of the subject.

The only comparison I could rely on was the reading I had at Trisha's premises some weeks before but nevertheless I did not know exactly what to expect. I was not to be disappointed.

There was no introduction - the curtains simply opened and Trisha appeared on stage. She was very smartly dressed in a long red dress with a feather boa and her eyes shone with excitement as she spoke with a speed of purpose which forced the audience to concentrate on every word. She explained how the evening would unfold and gave a brief explanation of her beliefs, saying that no one need be afraid or embarrassed as the messages she would relate would be brought with love.

She started with a name which was being given to her by a spirit, a child who gave her name as Annette. I looked around into the audience to find a reaction but there was none. Trisha probed further with a request for more detail from the insistent spirit. It was a peculiar sight to see Trisha speaking seemingly to some invisible person who chose to reply in secret and in silence, and yet it was acceptable for no one dared to laugh or interrupt.

It was at that very moment that I noticed a middle-aged lady two or three seats away from me on my row who appeared agitated as if troubled by what Trisha was saying. As Trisha related more information the more agitated the lady became. The spirit was of a child who passed over from meningitis when she was twelve years of age and it was her mother who was in the audience. Trisha asked why she wouldn't identify herself and take the message but there was no answer and so she said that she would have to move on to engage another spirit, but the little girl would not go and blocked the way for other spirits to come. Trisha told a stunned audience that if the lady concerned would not take the message the show would have to finish there and then.

You could have cut the atmosphere with a knife. People started to look around in desperation for a clue to identify the woman because it was clear that Trisha meant every word of what she was saying. Trisha told the audience that she would find the lady concerned and she told the spirit to identify her saying that it would have the effect of making a light appear about the appropriate person's head. Shortly afterwards she walked out into the audience and then pointed to the agitated lady two or three seats away from me, telling her that she had been identified as the lady concerned. With marked reluctance came the acknowledgement. The lady held up her hand and a sign of relief went around the theatre.

There was an interminably long silence before Trisha told the lady not to blame herself any longer for her daughter's death. It was like watching a tennis match involving first Trisha and then the woman in a compulsive exchange which ended with Trisha inviting the lady to speak to her in the interval, for the message was too personal to impart in front of an audience. During the interval I saw Trisha speaking to her and all appeared to be well.

In the second part of the performance there were messages for a variety of people, including one young woman whose father was in spirit who had come to apologise for something which had happened in the past. She gave his first name and then the bombshell that he had committed suicide by hanging himself some years earlier. The lady confirmed that what had been said was true, but then Trisha completed the message by saying simply that he was sorry and the lady would understand. She nodded in agreement as she wiped a tear from her face. It was then someone else's turn – mine.

Very much to my surprise Trisha turned to me and told me that my grandfather who was in spirit was there and he was holding a book and smiling. It could have meant a number of things but Trisha's translation was that there was a book which was to be most successful and it was to be my book. I resisted the compulsion to say, 'Oh really?'

After the performance concluded I went backstage to congratulate Trisha and seek some elaboration of my message. She described my grandfather who she visualised was wearing an old-fashioned uniform with a number of medals and manner of dress which was consistent with that worn by soldiers at the turn of the century. My mother who had travelled with me reminded me that my grandfather served in the forces at the turn of the century and was a much decorated soldier, so we were able to confirm his identity.

Just before I left I asked Trisha about the girl whose father had come to apologise, as it seemed to me to be a strange set of circumstances which seemed incomplete, but my curiosity surrounded his suicide. I wondered if that was the reason for his apology and she nodded gravely and told me that this man had abused his daughter and when the police were to arrest him he could not face the consequences and so had taken his own life.

We had a long conversation during which Trisha explained some of her history and in particular her time in the convent and how she arrived there, and then of course there was Hong Kong. There was something about her story which fascinated me, and even more her incredible ability to surprise, amuse and astonish with information she could not have gleaned from any source other than from the person who was supplying it. Remarkable though it may seem there could be no doubt that those people were dead.

The following day at home I was discussing the previous night's events and I expressed the view that Trisha's was a remarkable story and one which should be the subject of a book. Just then the telephone rang and it was Trisha who simply asked me to answer a question 'yes' or 'no'. For some inexplicable reason I did not seek an explanation.

"Is it you?" she asked. I told her that if she meant would I write her book then the answer was yes, and then she went on to explain about her friend Jane and the prediction she had made. The description fitted me. I was fifty years of age and my hair was beginning to turn grey. I was born of the twins, a Gemini, and my initials were 'S', but most important of all I was writing the book of the life story of a famous man, namely Charlie Williams.

Despite other offers I chose to write Trisha's story but I needed to know much more about Spiritualism and if possible to understand its philosophy. I was not to be disappointed.

THE BOOK

Trisha and I decided that we would meet on as regular a basis as time would allow and I would attend as many performances as I could with a view to improving my understanding of the subject and also to acquire material to write this book. We would meet at a nice pub near Clumber Park in Nottinghamshire, which was open all day and set in pleasant surroundings. Our meetings would last approximately four hours during which time we would discuss many things which enabled me to gain something of an insight into a most complex and remarkable character.

I found it difficult to forget however, that I was a solicitor who had spent the majority of my working life cross-examining people to get to the root of a case by posing the same questions in a different way. It was a formula I used to catch out witnesses who were less than truthful, but no matter how hard I tried to detach that philosophy from this project I found myself repeating the tactic almost automatically. I suppose I was sceptical at first but I was to see evidence which satisfied me that she was truly in contact with the spirit world leading me to be her staunchest ally when her beliefs were called into question. It was not an easy task for either of us. Her life in Hong Kong was particularly difficult for her to deal with. It was an era which had involved so much trauma that she had hidden the facts from her memory, such was the difficulty of recall.

As she unfolded the whole of the story I witnessed the pain which my questioning was causing, and yet I believe that it helped Trisha to come to terms with her past. As she dredged up each sordid detail I could see the colour drain from her face, so much so that I suggested we move on. It was as if she was purging her soul and yet I felt terribly guilty because for the first time I became aware of the enormity of what she had gone through as a child. I believe that it was a wonder she had not gone completely mad.

I enjoyed the performances, which helped me gain an insight into her beliefs and the unique way in which she was able to communicate to an audience.

I found that many people would not believe that there were no tricks in her performances and that she could not possibly have collected so much information about the life of a stranger. One of my friends is Neil Crossland, a local businessman who had worked in showbusiness for nearly forty years and when I discussed the topic with him he was convinced that all mediums were charlatans who made their point by using a number of 'plants' in the audience. I scoffed at such a suggestion which made Neil believe that I was in the grip of some form of religious cult, as did some of my other close friends who were similarly disposed. I had already decided that I would help Trisha formulate a concert tour and play a number of venues out of her area, so that more people could become acquainted with her remarkable gift. Neil is an expert at organising such events and so I discussed the subject with him at length but as always he was honest and even blunt in outlining his scepticism.

With this in mind I decided to invite Trisha to my house to enable her to give a demonstration for the benefit of a dozen or so of my friends. I invited an interesting mix of people, including journalists and my friend the BBC broadcaster John Holmes from Radio Derby with his wife Kate. My great friend Chris Good was there too with his wife and son, and there were other friends Tom and Gill Furniss, Ernie Booth and his partner Marge and Neil with his wife Maureen. I was so confident in Trisha's ability that I thought I would let the doubters and dissenters see for themselves.

The setting was my dining room, which did not really lend itself to such a function but I made the appropriate arrangements under the guise of a dinner party with a difference. Trisha arrived at about 7pm and began her preparations by going through the procedure she always adopted, including the saying of prayers in each corner of the room where the demonstration would take place.

Her other requirements were simple – a jug of water and a glass at the ready, as the consumption of water helped to conduct the energy required with the delivery of messages from the spirit world. Her only other requirement was that no one would speak to her before the performance or give her any information about any of the people present.

Inevitably my guests caught sight of Trisha as she came in and I noticed how they were all drawn to her as they scrutinised her every move. Some people stand out in a crowd and you cannot help but notice them, Trisha is one such person. After she had completed her preparations she left the room and went to sit in the study. She waited for me to explain to my guests what would happen and how best they could co-operate to enhance the demonstration, whereupon she entered the room to a modest round of applause. She looked around the audience and made assessments of the auras of the guests until she focused her attention upon Kate Holmes. I had known her husband John for some time, but I had only met Kate on two other occasions and consequently I was not privy to information about her personal life, and particularly not about her health.

Trisha began to speak to Kate and asked if she had any objections to being involved in the experiment. She agreed and Trisha promptly told her that she had previously endured a mastectomy. I had no knowledge of that operation as John and I had never discussed it and the revelation caused me to pay particular attention to the rest of the group, for I was not only interested in what Trisha told Kate but I was entranced by watching the faces of the other members as they looked on in disbelief when Kate confirmed what Trisha had said.

She dealt with her health at length, pointing out that at some stage in the future there would be another cause for concern about her condition. Fortunately this would not be a resumption of the original cancer which had eaten away at her in the past but would be some form of complaint which produced similar symptoms. She then spoke of Kate's children and their current problems with a degree of accuracy which caused John to partake of a sharp intake of breath.

In order to support what she had been saying Trisha turned to the question of evidence. Evidence is when she passes on some information to the subject which is given to her by spirit which is so obscure that only the subject or those close to her or him can know about it. If I have seen this happen once I have seen it happen a thousand times since I first met her and on this occasion the evidence was of exceptional quality. She told Kate of a burglary which had occurred at her house some years past in which almost all of her jewellery was stolen. Kate confirmed that such an incident had taken place and with a smile of recognition Trisha continued to tell her that her mother had given her this information from spirit. The old lady had passed on some years before and went on to tell Trisha that there was one item of jewellery, namely a gold locket and chain, which had been spared the clutches of the thief as it had been placed in the pocket of a coat with a view to repairing some damage. Trisha went on to tell her that after the burglary she had occasion to wear the coat and she found the locket and chain safe and sound. Ironically that particular piece of jewellery belonged to her mother.

The group were amazed, even the sceptical Neil Crossland, who, I could see, was busily working-out in his mind some formula which would explain away how Trisha had deduced these facts.

With faltering speech Kate confirmed what Trisha had said.

Trisha then turned to my old friend Chris Good. Prior to that meeting I would have said that there was little about Chris that I did not know and vice versa. We had been friends for over forty years and were extremely close to the extent that we were like brothers, so I doubted that there would be anything which would surprise me. I was wrong.

She spoke of Chris's father Arthur, who had passed away many years before and with whom Chris had enjoyed an excellent relationship. But even after so many years he still missed him, although the passage of time had eased the pain which grief had inflicted.

Trisha confirmed a number of factors from Chris's childhood and like the others before him he was visibly moved at some of the information which was being given, but the most fascinating feature of the reading was the subject of his health. Apparently some weeks before Chris had noticed a lump in the right hand side of his groin. I suppose most men would have thought the worst, and so did he, with the result that he confined the subject of his fears to his wife Pat. Trisha told him that his father was confirming that Chris had seen two doctors concerning the complaint, the first his general practitioner and the second a specialist. Chris nodded grimly in agreement.

Trisha continued to tell him that he would get an answer from the specialist within a matter of days and she was pleased to tell him that the growth was not cancerous but some form of cyst. I could not help but interject both out of personal concern but also to assure the rest of the gathering, and I pointed out that Chris had never mentioned the ailment to me. Chris agreed and said that he had not wanted to worry anyone and consequently he and Pat decided to keep the matter to themselves and even his son was not aware of what was happening.   Chris had been a sceptic but he was changing his view the more the evening progressed.

Within the next few days Chris received a letter from his doctor which confirmed the findings of the specialist.   He had a cyst in the right hand side of his groin, which was non-malignant and was not considered operable unless it caused him any discomfort.   It was difficult to imagine greater evidence other than this.

The evening had turned into a remarkable event and it seemed as though every member of the group was going to be treated to a message but Neil looked on suspiciously, still sceptical despite the incredible evidence which unfolded.

As is often the case, the best was saved until last.   The doubting Thomas of the gathering was undoubtedly Neil Crossland.   He had suffered ill-health and some years before he had been found to be suffering from a malignant tumour in his brain. Fortunately, the treatment he had been given arrested the growth of the tumour and he went into remission. Thankfully, he is still clear of danger although he attends the hospital annually for the customary checks.

Trisha picked up on the health problem by viewing his aura. The aura is a combination of our mind, body and spirit and takes the form of a wreath of light surrounding an object that emits radiation. Scientists recognise the existence of electro-magnetic and other types of radiation emitted by everybody and they can be measured accurately and the electro-magnetic radiation that creates auras can be calibrated.

A Russian research team called The Kirlians devised a method of photography which would capture the aura on the skin of a living body by means of high voltage electricity which imprints the picture onto a metal sheet. Now, with the aid of Kirlian photography, anyone may see a map of his aura or even the colours in it. Some people see the aura as a ball or egg-shaped object containing the human body, but most describe it as roughly outlining the contours of the body, the thickness of which has been described as an inch thick, whilst others claim it is up to twelve inches.

The aura does not disappear and neither can it be damaged; it just exists and is worn rather like a garment. It consists of many different colours blended together, in non-uniform sections which are layered, somewhat misty and form planes of colour which reflect the person's body and soul. The different colours of the aura represent a number of things. A white aura exists in every living body. A new-born baby has a pure white aura but with the passage of time the white will disappear and other colours will prevail, proving that somehow the imprint of life is fading. A white aura signifies purity and health. A black aura indicates a serious disease, whereas a grey signifies danger indicating that the white aura is damaged. The other colours represent a number of conditions too complicated to deal with here.

There was a grey area centred around Neil's head where the tumour was situated and Trisha was able to see the problem. She visualised a flower in the form of a rose which was symbolic and did not necessarily mean that someone had brought flowers or had flowers given. It was her task to translate the meaning of the symbol into a message and to trace the recipient. To enable her to understand the meaning of the symbol, she had to pose a number of questions in order to identify for whom the message was intended and what the picture of a rose meant. No one claimed to have bought a rose that day and so Trisha tried a different tack. She asked the group if they were related to someone in spirit called Rose and then from obscurity at the back of the room Neil said that he knew such a woman who had died quite a short time before. I could not help but smile, for this was just the sort of message that was needed to convince Neil that there was something worthy of consideration in what Trisha was saying.

Having identified the connection Trisha pursued the point and then totally out of the blue she told Neil that the message she was getting was that he had asked Rose to communicate with him in some way that very evening. We were all perplexed because not one of our group knew of this lady, but Neil was more than forthcoming with an explanation.

He told us that only a relatively short time before, the mother of one of his closest friends had died. He had been discussing the forthcoming evening with his wife Maureen that afternoon and had been highly critical of clairvoyants and mediums generally, but during the discussion he had told Maureen that he would only be convinced of Trisha's ability if his friend Rose should in some way make contact with him that night. He did not believe that this would be possible, although I suspected that there must have been something in the back of his mind which made him want to believe the possibility.

From that moment Neil moved from a state of disbelief to reluctant acceptance, particularly when Trisha gave him some home truths about his business which she could not have known from any other source. Neil was amazed and for once he was unable to come up with an explanation of his own, but he did offer to put on a show with Trisha as its star.

Neil's work for his charity, 'Top Turns' had achieved great things for sick and disadvantaged children and here was his opportunity to bring something new to the stage, and for us to bring Trisha's work to the attention of a wider audience. It was just the start we needed.

The evening was a great success and Trisha had been transformed from just 'another fortune teller' to someone who should be taken extremely seriously. Even the great sceptic Neil Crossland became a believer and how proud I was of the way that Trisha proved her point.

We had a magnificent dinner during which the topic of conversation remained the same. Trisha explained her beliefs and points of view to an already converted audience and afterwards Neil spoke continually about a number of performances for his charity and mentioned a number of possible venues.

At our next meeting Trisha and I decided that we would work with Neil for a limited number of dates and also arrange a number of our own performances by hiring theatres ourselves. At that time other than in her own area she was unknown, but my intuition told me that within a short time word soon spread; the difficulty was getting the venues and covering our costs. Nevertheless, we both felt that this was the right direction to take and after all there was no doubting her ability and the belief that this was what destiny had decreed for her. The ensuing months involved a great deal of hard work, but the reward was to be forthcoming in excitement, anticipation and a great deal of satisfaction.

THE PERFORMANCE

Over the ensuing weeks I had a number of meetings with Trisha concerning our preparations for the book. We would talk about Spiritualism and her beliefs for hours and it would only be when the meeting was about to close that we would spend fifteen or twenty minutes working on the book. I attended all of her demonstrations and as the 'looker-on sees most of the game' I was able to visualise a number of improvements which related to the presentation. Trisha listened intently to my suggestions, and adopted a number which she thought were constructive. I felt that from the point of view of general audience enjoyment a little more of the mystic should be maintained and I also believed that she should have a proper introduction with someone explaining what the performance would entail and what was expected of the audience. I talked myself into the job of acting as Master of Ceremonies, but by then I had begun to grasp the basic rudiments of Spiritualism and together with my natural yen for performance, Trisha found that my imput was mutually helpful. The more exhibitions I attended the more I became convinced as to life after death and the existence of the spirit world as time after time I was seeing irrefutable evidence that would satisfy any jury, that there was something there, some higher agency who knew all things.

Nevertheless I had so many questions, some of which I found answered at Trisha's performances, some I found by just discussing circumstances with her and some I found from books.

I scrutinised the audience as the fortunate recipients of messages listened intently to every word as Trisha amused informed and amazed the gatherings.

It was not all plain sailing, we didn't just book a theatre, sell all the tickets and convert every follower, for it was as much a learning curve for Trisha as much as it was for me. The theatres would always begin with the playing of her favourite music which gave her spiritual inspiration and which added a calmness and serenity to the proceedings as people entered the auditorium. My tendency to attempt to turn the meeting into some kind of show sometimes met with a polite and most kindly rebuke, as my enthusiasm towards the entertainment side of the performance perhaps outweighed the spiritual. Fortunately our openness and honesty with each other avoided confrontations and arguments and any misunderstandings were easily resolved by an open exchange of views.

The major difficulty was in making people aware, not only who Trisha was, but just how fluent a Medium she had become. The South Yorkshire area has its devotees of the subject but Trisha is much more than just a soothsayer, with her sparkling wit and desire to entertain and yet inform, and these qualities were to become a hallmark of her presentation.

I went to watch other Mediums and their demonstrations and whilst the general pattern was the same I found that there was something extra special about Trisha's performances which I did not find with the others, good though many of them were. Each demonstration filled me with anticipation, and the excitement was always intense. Would she be able to maintain the same standard? Would the spirits be kind to her in supporting her with evidence and more importantly would the audience respond and relate to her? Audiences varied from marked reluctance to incredible enthusiasm and it was interesting to see how many sceptics turned up, whatever their reasons were for so doing. It was a never-ending source of surprise to me that they would want to attend at all if they had neither interest nor sympathy in what was happening, but Trisha carried on defying the sceptics and converting many to the cause, not only with the gift of clairvoyance but her unique way of presenting it to an audience.

Unfortunately, the concerts were all localised and we really needed the opportunity which would catapult her into national status to fulfil Jane's prophecy, but I was soon to learn that this would not be achieved overnight.

Over the months that the book was in preparation we systematically fine-tuned the presentation and along the way formed a most fulfilling partnership, which uncharacteristically left me in the background in charge of the organisation, whilst Trisha concentrated on the front of house and the performance.. The beginnings were small and involved a great deal of hard work as we were a long way from playing to bigger audiences wider afield.

Our first steps were quite tentative but then they had to be, the costs in setting-up a concert tour were substantial and there was always the question of advance publicity, posters, printing, organisation of venues, contractual liabilities and even copyright charges for the music which we played before and during the shows. I firmly believed that it was only a matter of time before we would achieve a measure of success and Trisha would achieve her destiny.

The hardest work was in the production of this book which took more and more of my time as I tried to juggle my firm's affairs with my own, and yet do justice to both. It was becoming increasingly obvious that one would have to go. There was no real difficulty in the choice except I had a mortgage and an overdraft and a number of staff to take into account, but in the end I had my own future to think of and after thirty-five years in the legal profession I was looking for something new. The difficulty was the office partnership and the responsibility that it had placed upon my shoulders.

With my mind in turmoil I soldiered on, working as many as twenty hours a day, but inevitably my health began to suffer, which caused Trisha to express a great deal of concern about my welfare. In the past I had worked extremely hard to satisfy the expectations placed upon me by a number of agencies and whilst I was throwing a large number of balls into the air, I seemed to be one hand short in catching them when they all came down. I knew that decisions would have to be made and yet somehow I also knew what I had to do and it was as if I had been trained in all manner of things, albeit superficially, but with a specific purpose in mind. I was convinced that that purpose was connected with Trisha's beliefs.

At one of the shows I decided to record what happened on video so that audiences would have a recording to take home with them. I saw no possible objection to a commercial aspect of the relationship and so I called in my friend Robin Colvill, one of the founder members of the television show group 'The Grumbleweeds' to help.

Robin is a very talented man, not only a brilliant comedian but an accomplished hypnotist and cameraman. His showbusiness background gave him an insight into what I wanted in the video recording. He used the very latest digital camera equipment to film a full show, which took place at The Palace Theatre, Mansfield. The great actor and comedian Bobby Knutt was our guest of honour and there was a greetings card from Charlie Williams himself, all the way from America. The proceedings were filmed with two cameras and Robin and his assistant Ken Webster were able to record the reactions of the audience and play both on a split-screen recording. The result was an interesting film highlighting the very best of Trisha's work, suitable for all and not only devotees.

I had to reconcile the commercial aspect of what I was doing with the greater cause of Spiritualism but I believed that I was truly helping to spread the word. As such the two subjects were interlocked and in any event the costs of the tours and other charges had to be met from somewhere.

The most rewarding thing of all was the sight of a satisfied audience leaving the theatre full of comment and recalling the moments which interested them most. The people who received messages were the most elated of all, particularly if they had contact with a loved one. The knowledge that they were happy and in a much better place did so much to ease the grief at the loss of such a person. I spoke to so many people who were so happy to have received such messages that they could think and talk of nothing else, such was their gratitude.

Trisha enjoyed dealing with the sceptics best of all, as I suppose it was the challenge which appealed to her most, but whoever was watching and listening, everyone had to admit that the gatherings were not only interesting and exciting but a great deal of fun.

I gave her a lift home after one evening's presentation. I was invited in to have something to eat and drink. I was sitting in the front room whilst Trisha was busily preparing supper and doing at least two other jobs at the same time. She was consequently having difficulty concentrating on conversation. I looked around the room and noticed a sculpture of praying hands which was draped with a sort of chain leading to a crucifix.

As she delivered my drink I asked her where she had got the crucifix, and as she ran out of the room to retrieve a boiling pot she told me it was the only thing she owned which had belonged to her mother. Just then the curse of the modern age, my mobile phone rang, the caller enquiring about our next show. The interest had already begun.

After another of our meetings I noticed that Trisha was unwell. There were dark patches under her eyes and she looked very tired. I asked her what was wrong and she recounted the events of the previous day when she had been walking in the park with her children.

She had begun to feel out of sorts, although it was neither marked by nausea nor pain. It was a feeling she had not experienced before, although at first she thought it might be something related to diabetes. The condition continued until she was forced to sit on a nearby park bench. She described the feeling as 'being taken over' with her thought processes being 'put to sleep', but subsequently her children were horrified to see Trisha's face begin to change its shape and her voice begin to deepen. Whilst her physical characteristics had changed, her mind wrestled with that of another who was attempting to take over her mind. Fantastic though it may seem, Trisha had begun to enter into a phase of transfiguration where the spirit of a person who has passed over manifests itself in the physical framework of a human being.

Simply stated, a transfiguration is the fashioning and altering of a body from the mould intended by nature.

What concerned Trisha was the fact that this transfiguration had taken place without warning and other than in a controlled situation. It was something that she would not only have to come to terms with and control but it was the last great step to take before Trisha could truly lay claim to being one of the best of Mediums.

At the Edwinstowe Spiritualist Church on Sunday 22 August 1999 Trisha was giving a presentation when it happened again in front of a church of over fifty witnesses. Fortunately on that occasion she was able to control the manifestation. It is beyond the scope of my knowledge to know how it happens, but it is just another page in a remarkable story about an even more remarkable woman.

There are those who would say she is mad or from the more courteous sceptics, eccentric at least. I do not criticise them, they are entitled to their opinion, but more often than not, it is based upon supposition without full knowledge of the facts and the evidence which supports her.

I suppose my training as a lawyer has helped me and in her defence I can say that I have witnessed all manner of extraordinary things and such substantial evidence as proves to me beyond reasonable doubt that she is in touch with the spirit world. For my own peace of mind, I have used scepticism in its most positive form to seek and to enquire, and most of all to see the evidence for myself. I can do no more than relate the facts and it is for the reader to make his or her own decision. At the very least I would suggest that they see one of her demonstrations when I know that I will be asked those most frequently recurring questions:

"How does she do it?" or "What research has she done about me?"

The answer is simply that she doesn't do any research at all. She is the instrument of the spirit world who has been chosen to explain as best she can, the philosophy of Spiritualism by passing on messages from those no longer on this earthly plane, to those who are.

She cannot answer all the questions that are asked of her, but she can tell of her experiences and her beliefs in a way which will entertain and enthral as only she can.

THE FUTURE

Trisha was not impressed with the video recording of the Mansfield show because she said that she looked fat! I explained that videos had that effect and she should not be deterred, but it led to her losing two stones in weight in the ensuing months. During this time she made the ultimate sacrifice in giving up chocolate!

I was in negotiation with a number of theatres to bring Trisha's performance to a wider audience but the difficulty was that she was unknown out of her own area. The painstaking work of building her up to the press and the media had already begun, but it was surprising just how suspicious people were of the subject. When I mentioned it I was met with descriptions which varied between 'black magic', 'mumbo-jumbo' and 'Satanism'. The latter was the easiest to deal with for how could Satanism put grieving people's minds at rest and relieve their pain at the loss of a loved one? How could it be Satanism to laugh and have fun in the fond remembrance of people from the past? I rejected their arguments out of hand.

The other criticism was that our beliefs were thought by many to be contrary to the doctrine of Christianity. The great writer Sir Arthur Conan-Doyle, creator of the character Sherlock Holmes, was not only a writer and a Doctor of Medicine, but also a devotee of Spiritualism and President of the British College of Psychic Science. He said,

"Spiritualism is a system of thought and knowledge which can be reconciled with religion. The basic facts are the continuity of personality and the power of communication after death."

He believed that Spiritualism may be reconciled with any religion. Both Christianity and Spiritualism preach life after death and both recognise that the afterlife is influenced in its progress and happiness by conduct on this earth. They both believe in the existence of a world of spirits, good and evil, whom the Christians calls angels and devils and the Spiritualist calls guides and under-developed spirits. Conan-Doyle also believed that the Spiritualism was nearer to primitive Christianity than any other sect.

It is suggested that Spiritualists now can be divided into those who remain in their church and those who have formed a church of their own, but they are said to be roughly united upon seven central principles which are as follows:

1. The fatherhood of God.
2. The brotherhood of man.
3. The communion of saints and the ministry of angels.
4. Human survival of physical death.

5.   Personal responsibility.
6.   Compensation or retribution for good or evil deeds.
7.   Eternal progress open to every soul.

All these principles are compatible with ordinary Christianity with perhaps the exception of the fifth.

Spiritualists consider that Christ's earth life and death are an example rather than a redemption, where everyone is answerable for their own sins, and repentance will not preclude the individual from receiving his or her just desserts even though God's mercy is infinite.   But all circumstances will be taken into account before atonement is made.

I could not begin to understand fully all the complexities which surround the subject, but I was keen to learn and there was much to do.   Trisha had a thirty year advantage of experience over me, but she too had much to learn.   Quite where that left me was anyone's guess but it did introduce me to a new way of life with alternative beliefs.   I worked hard to banish the demons of negativity and depression which had haunted me for so many years, as I sought the answer to so many questions.   Why are there wars?   Why is there so much suffering in the world?   Why had Trisha's life been so blighted with tragedy?   I bought and borrowed books and attended lectures and seminars, and then of course there were the shows and readings.   My mind was bombarded with facts and explanations, so much so that there were times when I believed I was moving backwards but throughout all the set-backs Trisha's beliefs shone through like a beacon.

As more and more people came to visit our performances word spread about this remarkable woman, whose past experiences would make even the hardest of individuals wince. The task was to introduce her to a national audience and beyond that, who knows?

I had come to accept Spiritualism after over a year of research, although some would say this was too short a time to make such a decision, but I would disagree. It is a question of the quality of the evidence, and I had seen an abundance of it on a regular basis. And then there was Trisha herself. Despite every tragedy, every shortcoming and every retrograde step she never gave in but more importantly her beliefs were never forsaken. If anyone deserved success it was her. If anyone was entitled to find happiness and contentment it was her, and if anyone should find peace, well, I believe that she will.

She has travelled a long way, largely on her own, from those humble origins in a shoebox. What I have to do is to help her achieve those Silver Shoes.

EPILOGUE

I like stories with a happy ending when the hero rises up triumphantly and right and honour prevail.

How I have wished that this story could end in the same way; but then it is not quite over yet as Trisha continues her search for the silver shoes and we both pursue our respective journeys towards enlightenment.

As I began to write the final chapter of this book I realised that there were so many unanswered questions that I felt the responsibilities of authorship should extend to an attempted denouement before the last page was written.

I hope I make a reasonable attempt. I say attempt because I do not profess to fully understand the story myself. Doubtless a number of connotations can be placed upon this series of events making it all the more interesting to discuss and even argue about.

The concert tour has begun to take shape and I await with baited breath the result; but the questions and nagging doubts persisted.

Who gives Trisha her messages? Do the spirits represent good or bad? Why is it that only certain people can receive messages and the majority cannot? What happened to Ho and Heung? Above all, who were her true parents?

On a personal note I wondered about all the past years of study culminating in my small venture into the literary world. Was it truly for some greater purpose of potential benefit to others or just for myself? I hope that one day I will find out, but for the moment I will start with the messages.

Trisha not only hears voices but her subconscious mind shows her a series of symbols which she translates into information for submission to those intended to receive it. Generally speaking the recipients are amazed at the accuracy of what they hear.

I have watched her and listened intently over many hours of rapt attention both in private and in the company of others at theatres and churches. I have absolutely no doubt that her information is provided by some higher agency who is of spirit, and who represents universal love of which we are all a part. The depth and mysteries of this subject however are such that they deserve greater explanation than these pages will allow, and so I will move on.

169

Each of us has the ability to speak with the spirit world but only a few of us recognise and are aware of it. Consequently we have to rely upon 'mediums' who have identified and can deploy this wonderful gift; but of course it is not quite so easy as that.

So far as Ho and Heung were concerned, they were figures from the past. I was convinced that Heung had died in that terrible incident at the shanty, and I suspect that Ho had fallen too far from grace ever to be rehabilitated; contact has been impossible, and so maybe we will never know what happened to her.

I have continued to reflect upon my part in this affair, my personal experiences having been gained in over thirty-five years of a working life, which has steered me through a flirtation with showbusiness into the arena of the courtroom and finally into the writing of books. I do not believe that it has been a pointless exercise. There really must have been something more than just going through the motions of life. I am convinced it has all been for some special purpose.

These philosophical meanderings have understandably led me to reflect upon the way ahead. To this end my mind has returned to the past, and in particular to where Trisha's life started. During our earlier association we had discussed her parentage but her recollections turned upon the memory of a small child, limited by what she had been told at the convent and by Walter Smith following her adoption.

All she knows of her father is that he was a Romany gypsy called Star who disappeared from the area shortly after her birth. She believes that the gypsies would not accept her owing to her physical abnormalities, believing that some form of curse had imposed it.

Her mother on the other hand had been called Elizabeth, a very young girl of angelic features whose circumstances were such that she was unable to keep her baby and may have even concealed the pregnancy. It was all so confusing and seemed to defy any logical programme of discovery since the passage of time and the lack of any available family intermediaries from whom I could solicit information all conspired to work against me in my search for the truth.

I expressed my confusion at the end of one of our meetings, and as I was leaving, Trisha told me that the answers could be found within the manuscript of the story which I had so far composed. I did not quite realise what she was saying otherwise I would have probed more deeply, but on the journey home I reflected upon the conversation and began to search my memory to see if I could pick up any clues. In addition to the question of identity there was the question of secrecy. It was almost as if Trisha could not tell me the truth and yet neither could she hide behind a lie, and so when I got home I picked up the manuscript and began to read it. As I did so I began to recall what she had told me about the convent and Mr Smith's interest in her background. The key was in there somewhere, but where?

She had spoken of a novice nun at the convent who had volunteered to look after her but there was something about that nun which was important. Then I remembered a relatively small if obscure point concerning the nun's clothing;

'She wore a loose fitting habit which looked as though it had been made for someone else, but it was pristine and clearly new'.

Additionally there was the strange secret, which was based on the special relationship which existed between them, and the odd comment about Sister Marina's first reaction to the baby;

'... was one of relief mixed with a generous degree of sympathy'.

When Trisha reached the age of seven years there was the conversation when the Sister told her about the secret;

'It's our secret, but one day it will be for someone else to tell'.

Once again I referred back to the description of their relationship;

'... there was something else, something intangible within the good Sister's grasp, but beyond that of her charge which led to the affinity'.

Whilst I thought about that, another piece of information struck me with some force;

'Sister Marina neither knew how to break the news nor how to come to terms with it herself'.

This statement heralded some important news. What news? What would the picture look like if 'the news' was of Trisha's adoption by the Chinese couple? It was then that everything started to fit into place.

What if the nun's habit hid a pregnancy and the Sister volunteered to look after her own child? What if Sister Marina had managed to hide the pregnancy, albeit by a secretive route? It would explain her relief and her reaction to the baby's arrival and perhaps the opportunity to volunteer was one twist of fate too good to miss.

In one golden moment I remembered the crucifix draped around the sculpture of the praying hands, and the conversation we had after one of the shows. How on earth had I missed it? My only mitigation was that my thoughts had been disturbed by a mobile phonecall, which had annoyed me and changed the direction of my thinking;

'It's my mother's, it's the only thing I have of hers'.

The crucifix and the large chain-type attachment were the type worn by nuns around the waist of their habits.

Trisha had told me her mother's first name was Elizabeth and I must confess that the name had concealed the point from me until I found out that when someone enters a convent (in certain Orders) they adopt a name of the sisterhood. She was indeed Elizabeth, who had chosen to become Sister Marina.

This was the penultimate piece of the jigsaw. My assumption was that Sister Marina was Trisha's natural mother.

Unfortunately the 'secret' was still a puzzle and with my mind racing I looked at the clock. It was 4am and I was due at the office at 8am and the Magistrates Court at 9.30am but my thoughts were elsewhere. How could I sleep with such a problem dominating my very existence?

There was only one explanation; the secret was the relationship between the two of them. Sister Marina had told her charge what the relationship was, but why would Trisha keep it a secret for so long?

The answer came to me shortly before 5am. She could not break the promise to keep the secret even into adulthood and how could she be criticised for that? Discovery during those days at the convent would have threatened the very fabric of their existence and after all Sister Marina was all she then had.

The next morning I telephoned Trisha and arranged to meet her. The words of assurance from Sister Marina stood out in my mind;

'....*It is our secret, but one day it will be for someone else to tell*'.

Here was Trisha's opportunity to purge her contempt and take advantage of a release valve, which would free her from her promise. *I* would tell the secret.

I explained my views to her and almost in anti-climax Trisha agreed with me. It provided considerable relief to us both. It appeared that for once I had got it absolutely right and in doing so, Trisha had been released from her promise.

As we parted that day I watched her walk back to her house and turn and wave. I waved back and in so doing thought I saw the figure of a nun standing just behind her.

I dismissed it as being wishful thinking, with my subconscious mind playing tricks on me, but then again, perhaps it wasn't my imagination after all…………..

POST SCRIPT

I have included two of my favourite poems which mean a great deal to me.   I wanted to feature them in these pages.

Trisha

The Call

There is a voice that calls so sweet and clear,
From that ethereal world which is unseen,
Yet vanity of man won't let him hear
That voice, that is and has, forever been.

Since dawn of time, the beauty of its sound,
Has echoed through creation far and near.
A symphony of love, that knows no bounds,
The universal music of the spheres.

And even now that voice is calling still,
To each of us, who in the darkness tread,
To change our life, to answer spirits will,
To seek the light and find the way ahead.

No matter how you try, it's all in vain
For once you hear that call you must obey
That quiet voice will make its purpose plain,
It's talk for us each in a different way.

Yet walk along the path that spirit shows,
And you will find the greatest joy of all,
For truth is shown to everyone who knows,
And answers 'yes' to that eternal call.

Amen.

A Quiet Thought

As you wake every morning to greet each new day,
Why not stop for a moment and quietly pray.
To our Father who gives you his love and his care,
It takes little time to offer a prayer.

For each day is a journey on life's weary road,
But with spirit beside you you'll lighten your load;
You'll know life is filled with joy you can find,
If only you'll see, with eyes that aren't blind.

If you would but look, lift your eyes from the ground.
The beauty of spirit is there to be found.

It's there in the laughter of children at play,
It's there in the sunshine that brightens each day,
It's there all around you, not hidden from view,
Life's beauty, our Father, created for you.

The wealth of this world is not riches of gold,
True wealth is the joy in our hearts that we hold.
The truth that we share, upon which we call,
The beauty of spirit is God's gift to all

Amen

Also by Stephen D Smith:

HELL IS NOT FOR ANGELS

BOOZERS BALLCOCKS & BAIL

PLONKERS PLAINTIFFS & PLEAS

"CHARLIE" - THE CHARLIE WILLIAMS STORY

Coming Soon:

JUNKIES JUDGES & JAIL

All available from:
Neville-Douglas Publishing Ltd,
Clumber Lodge, Hemingfield Road,
Wombwell, Barnsley S73 OLY

Neville-Douglas Publishing Ltd
presents the book that was banned

HELL IS NOT
FOR ANGELS

by
Stephen D Smith

Subject of two BBC Rough Justice Programmes

On 13 July 1990 John Megson was convicted of murder at Leeds Crown Curt. The Judge gave him the mandatory life sentence and recommended that he serve no less than 15 years! John Megson was an innocent man and it was to take five years for justice to be done.

In April 1989, a camper was fatally stabbed after upsetting members of Megson's motorcycle gang, the Druids. Megson alone was convicted of the killing and because he refused to break the bikers' code of silence he went to prison for a crime he did not commit. For two years John's father tried to persuade him to name the real killer. He knew his son was innocent. He then contacted Steve Smith.

A single meeting with John in Wakefield Prison convinced a solicitor with 26 years in the legal profession that an innocent man was serving a life sentence for a murder he had not committed. He realised that "I was stuck with John Megson and he with me whether we liked it or not."

Pages: 264   **Size: 216x138**   **ISBN 1-901853-00-4**

Neville-Douglas Publishing Ltd
Clumber Lodge, Hemingfield Road,
Wombwell, Barnsley, Yorkshire S73 OLY
Tel: 01226 753324 Fax: 01226 758462

Neville-Douglas Publishing Ltd
present

Boozers
Ballcocks
&
Bail
by
Stephen D Smith

Boozers Ballcocks & Bail is a no-holds-barred account of the life of a thriving criminal law practice in an industrial northern town in the early eighties. It opens the door on the law in a totally honest and compelling way, giving an insight into the sometimes tragic, but often hilarious world of law courts, prison cells and solicitors' offices.

"..Steve Smith is the legal James Herriot." - Yorkshire Post

"This book will make you laugh." – Charlie Williams

Pages: 256   Size: 216x138   ISBN 1-871647-33-9

Neville-Douglas Publishing Ltd
Clumber Lodge, Hemingfield Road,
Wombwell, Barnsley, Yorkshire S73 0LY
Tel: 01226 753324 Fax: 01226 758462

Neville-Douglas Publishing Ltd
present

Plonkers
Plaintiffs
&
Pleas
by
Stephen D Smith

Plonkers Plaintiffs & Pleas is the sequel to the hilarious Boozers Ballcocks & Bail which was the first book in the comedy series relating what it is really like behind the closed doors of the legal profession. ***Plonkers Plaintiffs & Pleas*** continues the story with page after page of laugh out loud material.

"..Steve Smith is the legal James Herriot." - Yorkshire Post
" A hilarious book" - Charlie Williams

Pages: 256   **Size: 216x135**   **ISBN 1-901853-10-1**

Neville-Douglas Publishing Ltd
Clumber Lodge, Hemingfield Road,
Wombwell, Barnsley, Yorkshire S73 OLY
Tel: 01226 753324   Fax: 01226 758462